DESIGN**AMERICA**
presents

one-story
HOUSE PLANS

OVER 125 POPULAR HOME PLANS

DESIGNAMERICA

Current Printing (last digit)
10 9 8 7 6 5 4 3 2

Design America™ presents 1-Story - Over 125 Popular Home Plans
ISBN-13: 978-1-58678-015-9

DESIGN AMERICA, INC.™
designamerica.com

The homes on the cover are: Top, Plan #909-011D-0342 on page 64; Plan #909-101D-0059 on page 61, Warren Diggles Photography; Plan #909-076D-0280 on page 65; Bottom: Plan #011S-0090 at houseplansandmore.com; All plans available for purchase at houseplansandmore.com.

Home featured on page 1: Plan #909-011D-0311 on page 40.

CONTENTS

Top to bottom: Plan #909-101D-0045 on page 56; Plan #909-011D-0006 on page 20; Plan #909-161D-0013 on page 83; Plan #909-028D-0099 on page 37; Plan #909-055D-0748 on page 20; Plan #909-101D-0094 on page 45.

what's the right PLAN for you?

Choosing a house design is exciting, but can be a difficult task. Many factors play a role in what home plan is best for you and your family. To help you get started, we have pinpointed some of the major factors to consider when searching for your dream home. Take the time to evaluate your family's needs and you will have an easier time sorting through all of the house designs offered in this book.

BUDGET is the first thing to consider. Many items take part in this budget, from ordering the blueprints to the last doorknob purchased. When you find the perfect house plan, visit houseplansandmore.com and get a cost-to-build estimate to ensure that the finished home will be within your cost range. A cost-to-build report is a detailed summary that gives you the total cost to build a specific home in the zip code where you're planning to build. It is interactive, allowing you to adjust labor and material costs, and it's created on demand when ordered so all pricing is up-to-date. This valuable tool will help you know how much your dream home will cost before you buy plans (see page 106 for more information).

> **MAKE A LIST**
> Experts in the field suggest that the best way to determine your needs is to begin by listing everything you like or dislike about your current home.

FAMILY LIFESTYLE After your budget is deciphered, you need to assess you and your family's lifestyle needs. Think about the stage of life you are in now, and what stages you will be going through in the future. Ask yourself questions to figure out how much room you need now and if you will need room for expansion. Are you married? Do you have children? How many children do you plan on having? Are you an empty-nester? How long do you plan to live in this home?

Incorporate into your planning any frequent guests you may have, including elderly parents, grandchildren or adult children who may live with you.

Does your family entertain a lot? If so, think about the rooms you will need to do so. Will you need both formal and informal spaces? Do you need a gourmet kitchen? Do you need a game room and/or a wet bar?

FLOOR PLAN LAYOUTS When looking through these home plans, imagine yourself walking through the house. Consider the flow from the entry to the living, sleeping and gathering areas. Does the layout ensure privacy for the master bedroom? Does the garage enter near the kitchen for easy unloading? Does the placement of the windows provide enough privacy from any neighboring properties? Do you plan on using furniture you already have? Will this furniture fit in the appropriate rooms? When you find a plan you want to purchase, be sure to picture yourself actually living in it.

EXTERIOR SPACES With many different home styles throughout ranging from Traditional to Contemporary, flip through these pages and find which style of one-story home appeals to you the most and think about the neighborhood in which you plan to build. Also, think about how the house will fit on your site. Picture the landscaping you want to add to the lot. Using your imagination is key when choosing a home plan.

Choosing a house design can be an intimidating experience. Asking yourself these questions before you get started on the search will help you through the process. With our large selection of sizes and styles, we are certain you will find your dream home in this book.

10 steps to BUILDING your dream home

1 TALK TO A LENDER

If you plan to obtain a loan in order to build your new home, then it's best to find out first how much you can get approved for before selecting a home design. Knowing the financial information before you start looking for land or a home will keep you from selecting something out of your budget and turning a great experience into a major disappointment. Financing the home you plan to build is somewhat different than financing the purchase of an existing house. You're going to need thousands of dollars for land, labor, and materials. Chances are, you're going to have to borrow most of it. Therefore, you will probably need to obtain a construction loan. This is a short-term loan to pay for building your house. When the house is completed, the loan is paid off in full, usually out of the proceeds from your long-term mortgage loan.

2 DETERMINE NEEDS

Selecting the right home plan for your needs and lifestyle requires a lot of thought. Your new home is an investment, so you should consider not only your current needs, but also your future requirements. Versatility and the potential for converting certain areas to other uses could be an important factor later on. So, although a home office may seem unnecessary now, in years to come, the idea may seem ideal. Home plans that include flex spaces or bonus rooms can really adapt to your needs in the future.

3 CHOOSE A HOMESITE

The site for your new home will have a definite impact on the design you select. It's a good idea to select a home that will complement your site. This will save you time and money when building. Or, you can then modify a design to specifically accommodate your site. However, it will most likely make your home construction more costly than selecting a home plan suited for your lot right from the start. For example, if your land slopes, a walk-out basement works perfectly. If it's wooded, or has a lake in the back, an atrium ranch home is a perfect style to take advantage of surrounding backyard views.

SOME IMPORTANT CRITERIA TO CONSIDER WHEN SELECTING A HOMESITE:

- Improvements will have to be made including utilities, walks and driveways
- Convenience of the lot to work, school, shops, etc.
- Zoning requirements and property tax amounts
- Soil conditions at your future site
- Make sure the person or firm that sells you the land owns it free and clear

4 SELECT A HOME DESIGN

We've chosen the "best of the best" of the one-story home plans found at houseplansandmore.com to be featured in this book. With over 18,000 home plans from the best architects and designers across the country, this book includes the best variety of styles and sizes to suit the needs and tastes of a broad spectrum of homeowners.

5 GET THE COST TO BUILD

If you feel you have found "the" home, then before taking the step of purchasing house plans, order an estimated cost-to-build report for the exact zip code where you plan to build. Requesting this custom cost report created specifically for you will help educate you on all costs asso-

ciated with building your new home. Simply order this report and gain knowledge of the material and labor cost associated with the home you love. Not only does the report allow you to choose the quality of the materials, you can also select options in every aspect of the project from lot condition to contractor fees. This report will allow you to successfully manage your construction budget in all areas, clearly see where the majority of the costs lie, and save you money from start to finish.

A COST TO BUILD REPORT WILL DETERMINE THE OVERALL COST OF YOUR NEW HOME INCLUDING THESE 5 MAJOR EXPENSE CATEGORIES:

- Land
- Foundation
- Materials
- General Contractor's fee - Some rules-of-thumb that you may find useful are: (a) the total labor cost will generally run a little higher than your total material cost, but it's not unusual for a builder or general contractor to charge 15-20% of the combined cost for managing the overall project.
- Site improvements - don't forget to add in the cost of your site improvements such as utilities, driveway, sidewalks, landscaping, etc.

6 HIRE A CONTRACTOR

If you're inexperienced in construction, you'll probably want to hire a general contractor to manage the project. If you do not know a reputable general contractor, begin your search by contacting your local Home Builders Association to get references. Many states require building contractors to be licensed. If this is the case in your state, its licensing board is another referral source. Finding a reputable, quality-minded contractor is a key factor in ensuring that your new home is well constructed and is finished on time and within budget. It can be a smart decision to discuss the plan you like with your builder prior to ordering plans. They can guide you into choosing the right type of plan package option especially if you intend on doing some customizing to the design.

7 CUSTOMIZING

Sometimes your general contractor may want to be the one who makes the modifications you want to the home you've selected. But, sometimes they want to receive the plans ready to build. That is why we offer home plan modification services. Please see page 109 for specific information on the customizing process and how to get a free quote on the changes you want to make to a home before you buy the plans.

8 ORDER HOME PLANS

If you've found the home and are ready to order blueprints, we recommend ordering the PDF file format, which offers the most flexibility. A PDF file format will be emailed to you when you order, and it includes a copyright release from the designer, meaning you have the legal right to make changes to the plan if necessary as well as print out as many copies of the plan as you need for building the home one-time. You will be happy to have your blueprints saved electronically so they can easily be shared with your contractor, subcontractors, lender and local building officials. We do, however, offer several different types of plan package depending on your needs, so please refer to page 107 for all plan options available and choose the best one for your particular situation.

Another helpful component in the building process that is available for many of the house plans in this book is a material list. A material list includes not only a detailed list of materials, but it also indicates where various cuts of lumber and other building components are to be used. This will save your general contractor significant time and money since they won't have to create this list before building begins. If a material list is available for a home, it is indicated in the plan data box on the specific plan page in this book.

9 ORDER MATERIALS

You can order materials yourself, or have your contractor do it. Nevertheless, in order to thoroughly enjoy your new home you will want to personally select many of the materials that go into its construction. Today, home improvement stores offer a wide variety of quality building products. Only you can decide what specific types of windows, cabinets, bath fixtures, etc. will make your new home yours. Spend time early on in the construction process looking at the materials and products available.

10 MOVE IN

With some careful planning and organization, your new home will be built on schedule and ready for your move-in date. Be sure to have all of your important documents in place for the closing of your new home and then you'll be ready to move in and start living your dream.

Browse the pages of Design America™ presents One-Story Home Plans and discover over 125 of the most popular one-story designs offered today in a variety of sizes and styles to suit many tastes and budgets. From Craftsman and Country, to Modern and Traditional, there is a one-story home in this book for everyone, and with all of the amenities and features homeowners are looking for in a home today. Start your search for the perfect one-story home right now!

Top, left: Plan #909-149D-0011 on page 19; top, right: Plan #909-011D-0311 on page 40; bottom, left: Plan #909-051D-0981 on page 17; bottom, right: Plan #909-055D-1039 on page 41.

PLAN #909-155D-0047

Dimensions: 60' W x 80'4" D
Heated Sq. Ft.: 2,500
Bonus Sq. Ft.: 354
Bedrooms: 3   Bathrooms: 2½
Foundation: Slab or crawl space,
please specify when ordering
See index on page 104 for more information

FEATURES

- Modern farmhouse touches grace the interior of this attractive rustic-looking ranch home
- The vaulted great room has a centered fireplace directly across from the island in the kitchen creating an intimate and cozy feel
- The master suite boasts a bath with a free-standing tub, a separate shower, a double-sink vanity, and a huge walk-in closet with built-ins
- Two additional bedrooms share a full bath
- The optional second floor has an additional 354 square feet of living area
- 2-car front entry garage

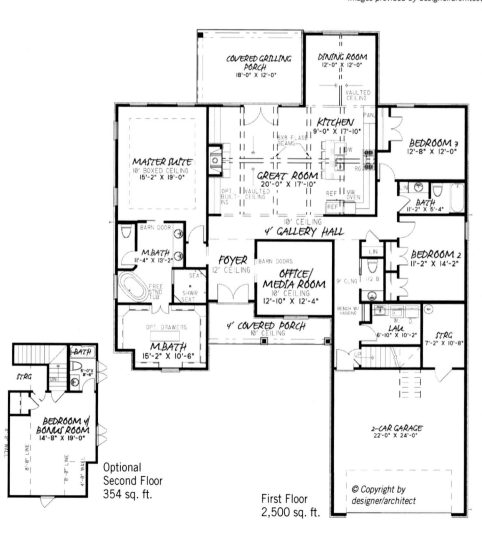

Optional
Second Floor
354 sq. ft.

First Floor
2,500 sq. ft.

© Copyright by
designer/architect

CALL 1-800-373-2646   **ONLINE** houseplansandmore.com

PLAN #909-013D-0208

Images provided by designer/architect

Dimensions:	36' W x 42'4" D
Heated Sq. Ft.:	953
Bedrooms: 2	Bathrooms: 1½

Foundation: Crawl space standard; basement or slab for an additional fee

See index on page 104 for more information

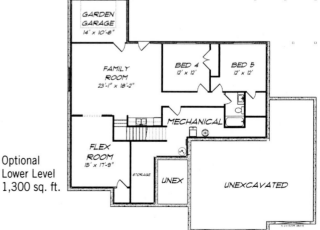

PLAN #909-159D-0007

Images provided by designer/architect

Dimensions:	64' W x 59' D
Heated Sq. Ft.:	1,850
Bonus Sq. Ft.:	1,300
Bedrooms: 3	Bathrooms: 2½
Exterior Walls:	2" x 6"

Foundation: Basement or walk-out basement, please specify when ordering

See index on page 104 for more information

First Floor
1,850 sq. ft.

Optional
Lower Level
1,300 sq. ft.

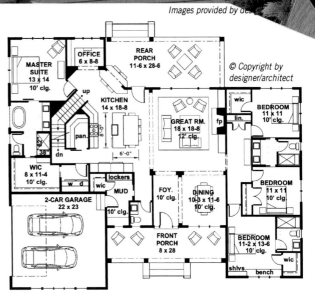

PLAN #909-091D-0523

Dimensions:	69' W x 57'6" D
Heated Sq. Ft.:	2,514
Bonus Sq. Ft.:	390
Bedrooms: 4	Bathrooms: 3½
Exterior Walls:	2" x 6"

Foundation: Basement standard; crawl space or slab for an additional fee

See index on page 104 for more information

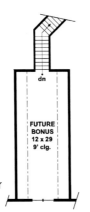

Optional Second Floor 390 sq. ft.

First Floor 2,514 sq. ft.

PLAN #909-052D-0158

Dimensions:	32'4" W x 54' D
Heated Sq. Ft.:	2,100
Bonus Sq. Ft.:	1,470
Bedrooms: 3	Bathrooms: 2
Foundation:	Walk-out basement

See index on page 104 for more information

Optional Second Floor 432 sq. ft.

First Floor 2,100 sq. ft.

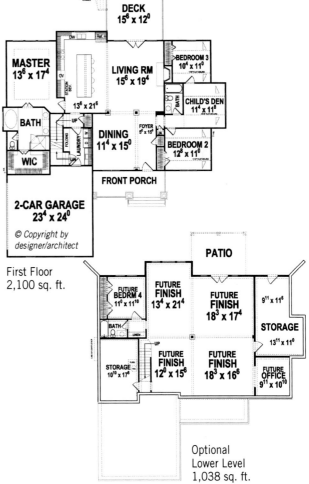

Optional Lower Level 1,038 sq. ft.

PLAN #909-101D-0107

Dimensions: 90' W x 72'6" D
Heated Sq. Ft.:   2,861
Bonus Sq. Ft.:   1,176
Bedrooms: 2   Bathrooms: 2½
Exterior Walls: 2" x 6"
Foundation: Basement, daylight basement or walk-out basement, please specify when ordering

See index on page 104 for more information

Images provided by designer/architect

FEATURES

- This wonderfully inviting home has all of the amenities homeowners love including an open-concept floor plan

- The kitchen features a massive island and a dining nook surrounded in windows

- There is both a mud room filled with storage as well as a laundry room with a sink

- The first floor guest bedroom has its own full bath and walk-in closet

- The optional lower level has an additional 1,176 square feet of living area and includes a rec room with a wet bar, and a spacious bedroom with direct bath access and a huge walk-in closet

- 2-car front entry garage, and a 2-car front entry tandem garage

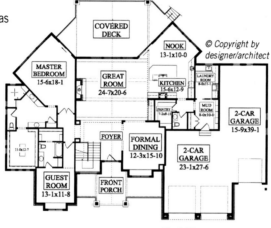

First Floor
2,861 sq. ft.

© Copyright by designer/architect

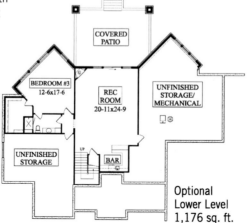

Optional
Lower Level
1,176 sq. ft.

PLAN #909-011D-0347

Dimensions: 113'4" W x 62'8" D
Heated Sq. Ft.:   2,910
Bedrooms: 3   Bathrooms: 3
Exterior Walls: 2" x 6"
Foundation: Post & beam or joisted continuous footings standard; slab or basement for an additional fee
See index on page 104 for more information

Images provided by designer/architect

FEATURES

- The foyer has 11' ceilings with wood columns into the vaulted great room straight ahead for an open and rustic interior
- The vaulted great room has gorgeous exposed beams, and a fireplace with built-ins
- An open floor plan combines the great room, kitchen, and dining room into one big "family triangle," with no walls to cramp the space
- The kitchen has an island with a double sink, 10' ceilings, and plenty of counterspace
- 3-car side entry garage

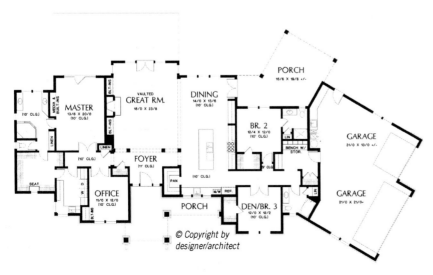

© Copyright by designer/architect

PLAN #909-091D-0517

Dimensions: 71' W x 76'8" D
Heated Sq. Ft.:   2,340
Bonus Sq. Ft.:   481
Bedrooms: 3   Bathrooms: 2½
Exterior Walls: 2" x 6"
Foundation: Basement or crawl space
standard; slab for an additional fee
See index on page 104 for more information

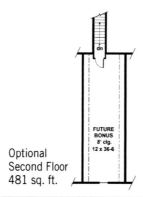

Optional
Second Floor
481 sq. ft.

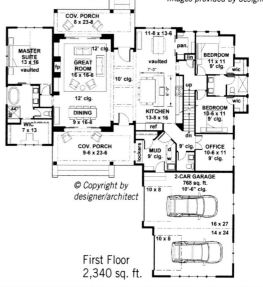

First Floor
2,340 sq. ft.

PLAN #909-007D-5060

Dimensions: 36' W x 46'4" D
Heated Sq. Ft.:   1,344
Bedrooms: 3   Bathrooms: 2
Foundation: Basement standard;
crawl space or slab for an additional
fee
See index on page 104 for more information

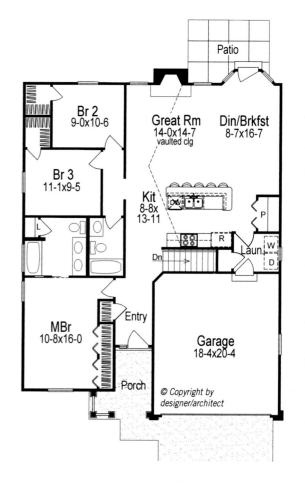

CALL 1-800-373-2646   ONLINE houseplansandmore.com

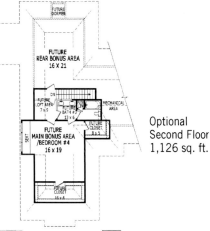

Optional
Second Floor
1,126 sq. ft.

PLAN #909-141D-0038

Dimensions: 93' W x 70'4" D
Heated Sq. Ft.:   2,700
Bonus Sq. Ft.:   1,126
Bedrooms: 3   Bathrooms: 2½
Foundation: Slab standard; crawl
space, basement or walk-out
basement for an additional fee

See index on page 104 for more information

© Copyright by
designer/architect

First Floor
2,700 sq. ft.

PLAN #909-013D-0245

Dimensions: 75'4" W x 59' D
Heated Sq. Ft.:   1,989
Bedrooms: 3   Bathrooms: 2½
Exterior Walls: 2" x 6"
Foundation: Slab standard; basement
or crawl space for an additional fee

See index on page 104 for more information

© Copyright by
designer/architect

PLAN #909-026D-1939

Dimensions: 60' W x 48' D
Heated Sq. Ft.: 1,635
Bedrooms: 3   Bathrooms: 2½
Foundation: Basement standard;
slab, crawl space or walk-out
basement for an additional fee
See index on page 104 for more information

Images provided by designer/architect

© Copyright by designer/architect

PLAN #909-101D-0057

Dimensions: 58' W x 90' D
Heated Sq. Ft.: 2,037
Bonus Sq. Ft.: 1,330
Bedrooms: 1   Bathrooms: 1½
Exterior Walls: 2" x 6"
Foundation: Walk-out basement
See index on page 104 for more information

Images provided by designer/architect

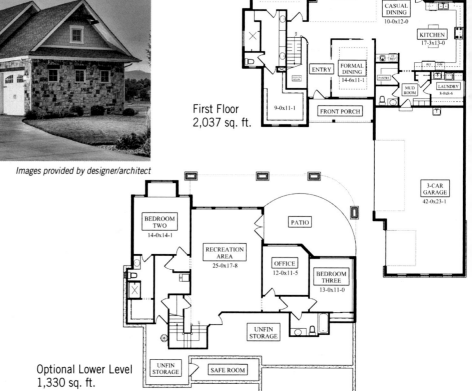

First Floor
2,037 sq. ft.

Optional Lower Level
1,330 sq. ft.

CALL 1-800-373-2646   ONLINE houseplansandmore.com

Images provided by designer/architect

PLAN #909-032D-0963

Dimensions:	34' W x 38' D
Heated Sq. Ft.:	1,178
Bonus Sq. Ft.:	1,178
Bedrooms: 1	Bathrooms: 1
Exterior Walls:	2" x 6"

Foundation: Basement standard;
crawl space, floating slab or
monolithic slab for an additional fee

See index on page 104 for more information

© Copyright by designer/architect

Optional Lower Level 1,178 sq. ft.

First Floor 1,178 sq. ft.

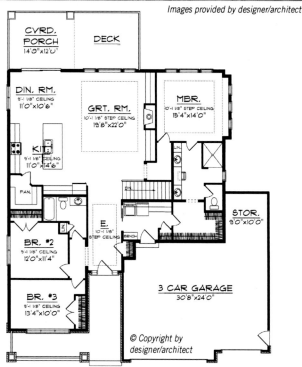

Images provided by designer/architect

PLAN #909-051D-0981

Dimensions:	55'4" W x 71'8" D
Heated Sq. Ft.:	2,005
Bedrooms: 3	Bathrooms: 2
Exterior Walls:	2" x 6"

Foundation: Basement standard;
crawl space or slab for an additional
fee

See index on page 104 for more information

© Copyright by designer/architect

CALL 1-800-373-2646   ONLINE houseplansandmore.com

PORCH

DINING
11/2 X 12/8
(9' CLG.)

SHELVES

VAULTED
MASTER
12/8 X 15/2

BUILT-INS

VAULTED
GREAT RM.
16/8 X 17/0

11/4 X 12/10

P

W D

REF

© Copyright by
designer/architect

MEDIA

LIN. LIN.

FOYER
(10' CLG.)

GARAGE
20/6 X 21/0

BR. 3/
DEN
10/6 X 11/4
(9' CLG.)

BR. 2
11/0 X 10/0
(9' CLG.)

PORCH

Images provided by designer/architect

PLAN #909-011D-0007

Dimensions: 50' W x 48' D
Heated Sq. Ft.:   1,580
Bedrooms: 3   Bathrooms: 2½
Exterior Walls: 2" x 6"
Foundation: Joisted crawl space,
TrusJoist floor system or post & beam
standard; slab or basement for an
additional fee

See index on page 104 for more information

PLAN #909-007D-0060

Dimensions: 38'8" W x 48'4" D
Heated Sq. Ft.:   1,268
Bedrooms: 3   Bathrooms: 2
Foundation: Basement standard;
crawl space or slab for an additional
fee

See index on page 104 for more information

Images provided by designer/architect

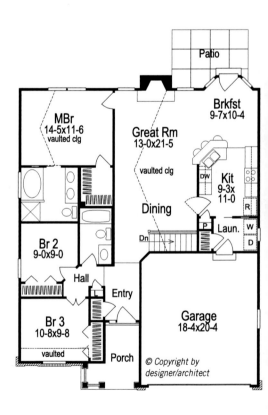

Patio

MBr
14-5x11-6
vaulted clg

Great Rm
13-0x21-5

Brkfst
9-7x10-4

vaulted clg

DW

Kit
9-3x
11-0

Dining

R

Br 2
9-0x9-0

Dn

P

Laun.

W

D

Hall

Entry

Br 3
10-8x9-8

Garage
18-4x20-4

vaulted

Porch

© Copyright by
designer/architect

18

CALL 1-800-373-2646   ONLINE houseplansandmore.com

Optional
Second Floor
612 sq. ft.

PLAN #909-149D-0011

Dimensions: 45' W x 65' D
Heated Sq. Ft.: 2,111
Bonus Sq. Ft.: 612
Bedrooms: 3 Bathrooms: 2½
Foundation: Slab standard; basement or crawl space for an additional fee

See index on page 104 for more information

Images provided by designer/architect

© Copyright by designer/architect

First Floor
2,111 sq. ft.

Images provided by designer/architect

PLAN #909-011D-0013

Dimensions: 60' W x 50' D
Heated Sq. Ft.: 2,001
Bedrooms: 3 Bathrooms: 2
Exterior Walls: 2" x 6"
Foundation: Joisted crawl space, post & beam or TrusJoist floor system standard; slab or basement for an additional fee

See index on page 104 for more information

© Copyright by designer/architect

PLAN #909-011D-0006

Dimensions: 70' W x 51' D
Heated Sq. Ft.:   1,873
Bedrooms: 3   Bathrooms: 2
Exterior Walls: 2" x 6"
Foundation: Joisted crawl space, post
& beam, or TrusJoist floor system
standard; slab or basement for an
additional fee

See index on page 104 for more information

PLAN #909-055D-0748

Dimensions: 67'2" W x 55'10" D
Heated Sq. Ft.:   2,525
Bedrooms: 4   Bathrooms: 3
Foundation: Crawl space or slab
standard; basement or walk-out
basement for an additional fee

See index on page 104 for more information

CALL 1-800-373-2646   **ONLINE** houseplansandmore.com

PLAN #909-051D-0972

Dimensions: 38' W x 74' D
Heated Sq. Ft.:   1,490
Bedrooms: 2   Bathrooms: 2
Exterior Walls: 2" x 6"
Foundation: Basement standard;
crawl space or slab for an additional
fee

See index on page 104 for more information

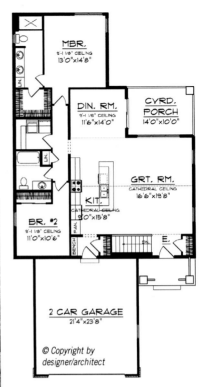

Images provided by designer/architect

Images provided by designer/architect

PLAN #909-056D-0098

Dimensions: 84'10" W x 61' D
Heated Sq. Ft.:   3,123
Bedrooms: 4   Bathrooms: 3
Foundation: Basement standard;
crawl space or slab for an additional
fee

See index on page 104 for more information

Lower Level
1,247 sq. ft.

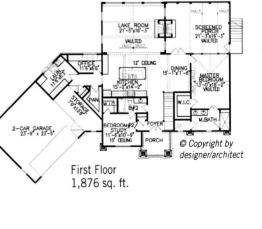

First Floor
1,876 sq. ft.

the stand-out features of a
1-STORY HOME

Countless homes continue to be designed to suit everyone's needs and desires. However, it is undeniable that many homeowners building a new home are looking for a long-term solution and a place to settle. No one puts the time and effort into building a new home they will only occupy for a mere moment. Keeping this in mind, it's important to recognize that building a one-story home is currently a popular and smart trend in new home construction.

Two-story homes have quite a bit to offer busy families and those who are budget conscious. They allow you to use the property to its fullest by building up rather than out and creating more living space without purchasing additional land. However, as the baby boomer generation grows older and their spending power allows them to continue to build new homes, space is not the first priority on aging minds. What good is great space if it becomes too difficult to access? Many baby boomers are looking to the future, building dream homes in which they can live out the rest of their lives. These homes are open, universally designed to handle physical limitations, and are still luxurious for entertaining family and friends. Retirees want plenty of space they can access independently. The one-story home is the dream home capable of fulfilling this desire. Multi-generational families also appreciate the ease one-story living brings thanks to its typically open floor plan and airy atmosphere making the home feel larger than its true size.

As you see from looking through the pages of this book, the one-story homes of today aren't lacking variety and architectural interest. One recommendation for making the most of a single story home is to create dynamic views. Varying window and ceiling heights and styles can be combined to create dramatic vistas from any point in a room. Spacious great rooms can boast grand ceilings and wall-sized picture windows, both of which are extremely popular in today's home designs. Not only can you expand the interior spaces of a one-story home out, but also up with soaring ceilings.

Here are some reasons why homeowners are so drawn to one-level living. With ease of movement, expansive room sizes, and convenience to and from every space, this type of floor plan is more popular than ever.

sloping lot, not a downfall

Sloping lots are anything but a downfall. Building a new home even if you don't have a flat plot of land is possible. Sloping lots offer the ideal location to build an atrium ranch home, for example. With sweeping windows along the entire rear wall, the home will be flooded with natural light. The added light creates dimension to the interior, while offering an impressive looking exterior. Or, how about building a ranch with a finished walk-out basement? If you have a sloping lot, select a home with a lower level that offers the possibility of expanding someday. A lower level can add the additional space needed every so often when entertaining, while providing space for hobbies, and overnight guests. Whether you're a wine collector looking for a wine cellar, enjoy a game of poker, or a huge movie buff, all of these things can be enjoyed in the comfort of a finished lower level.

maximize space

Combined spaces equal twice the function. One-story homes can offer more flexibility than multi-level homes. Living spaces without another level overhead permit vaulted ceilings, dramatic windows and the use of skylights or transoms to add spaciousness and natural light. Many ranch homes offer open floor plans created by combining the great room, dining space and kitchen to form the main gathering place. These areas when topped with a vaulted ceiling provide an impressive and highly functional space. Less walls means more square footage being maximized.

easy entertaining

Like previously mentioned, with many one-story homes having the ability to finish a lower level, an open lower level with state-of-the-art amenities is perfect for families that love to entertain and have frequent guests. While, the homeowners are still able to maintain a sense of privacy on the main level. A lower level is ideal for having fun with family and friends, or enjoying your favorite hobbies.

expand

Move one-story living to the outdoors with an amazing outdoor living space that is now a mainstay in new homebuilding. Many one-stories include fantastic outdoor living spaces, great for entertaining, everyday living, or enjoying a hobby like gardening. An outdoor kitchen is a fantastic amenity that keeps the cook and guests in close proximity to one another. And, an ever-popular outdoor fireplace warms an outdoor area so it can be enjoyed all year long. These spaces expand living beyond a home's walls and many offer a very seamless transition between the indoor and outdoor spaces.

special details

Amenities are found throughout every home no matter how many floors it has, but decorative ceilings and unique lighting can really enhance a one-story home quite easily and effectively. Seamless decorating from room to room creates a more open feel as well.

One-story homes are increasingly popular because they make a perfect starter home for new homeowners, while also having an ideal layout for those downsizing, or retiring. While a choice of homes is largely based on personal preference, one-story homes should be kept in mind when determining what home to build. One-story abodes have quite a bit to offer, just as every dream home should.

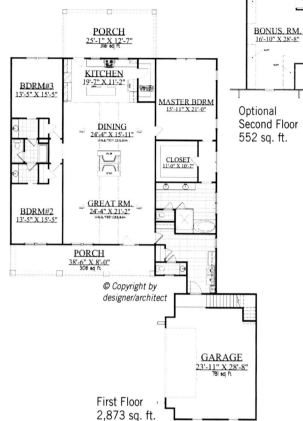

PORCH
25'-1" X 12'-7"
316 sq ft

KITCHEN
19'-7" X 11'-2"

BDRM#3
13'-5" X 15'-5"

MASTER BDRM
15'-11" X 21'-0"

DINING
24'-4" X 15'-11"
VAULTED CEILING

CLOSET
11'-0" X 10'-7"

BDRM#2
13'-5" X 15'-5"

GREAT RM.
24'-4" X 21'-2"
VAULTED CEILING

PORCH
38'-6" X 8'-0"
308 sq ft

© Copyright by
designer/architect

GARAGE
23'-11" X 28'-8"
791 sq ft

First Floor
2,873 sq. ft.

BONUS. RM.
16'-10" X 28'-8"

Optional
Second Floor
552 sq. ft.

PLAN #909-157D-0023

Dimensions: 65'11" W x 107' D
Heated Sq. Ft.: 2,873
Bonus Sq. Ft.: 552
Bedrooms: 3   Bathrooms: 2½
Foundation: Crawl space standard;
slab for an additional fee
See index on page 104 for more information

Images provided by designer/architect

PLAN #909-167D-0006

Dimensions: 68'11" W x 69'10" D
Heated Sq. Ft.: 2,939
Bedrooms: 4   Bathrooms: 3½
Exterior Walls: 2" x 6"
Foundation: Slab standard; crawl
space for an additional fee
See index on page 104 for more information

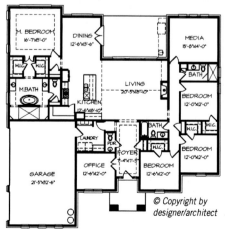

M. BEDROOM
16'-7"X15'-0"

DINING
12'-6"X13'-6"

MEDIA
15'-8"X14'-0"

M.BATH

BATH

LIVING
20'-5"X19'-0"

KITCHEN
12'-6"X18'-0"

BEDROOM
12'-0"X12'-0"

LAUNDRY

BATH

GARAGE
21'-5"X32'-6"

OFFICE
12'-6"X12'-0"

PDR

FOYER

BEDROOM
12'-6"X12'-0"

BEDROOM
12'-0"X12'-0"

© Copyright by
designer/architect

Images provided by designer/architect

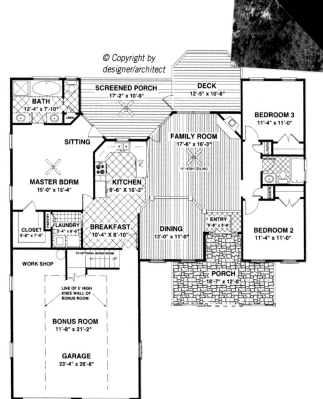

Images provided by designer/architect

PLAN #909-013D-0134

Dimensions: 55' W x 58' D
Heated Sq. Ft.: 1,496
Bonus Sq. Ft.: 301
Bedrooms: 3   Bathrooms: 2
Foundation: Slab standard; crawl space or basement for an additional fee

See index on page 104 for more information

Floor plan labels:
BATH 12'-4" x 7'-10"
SCREENED PORCH 17'-2" x 10'-9"
DECK 12'-5" x 10'-8"
BEDROOM 3 11'-4" x 11'-0"
SITTING
FAMILY ROOM 17'-6" x 16'-3"
10' HIGH CEILING
MASTER BDRM 15'-0" x 15'-4"
KITCHEN 9'-6" x 10'-2"
BEDROOM 2 11'-4" x 11'-0"
CLOSET 5'-8" x 7'-0"
BREAKFAST 10'-4" x 8'-10"
DINING 12'-0" x 11'-0"
ENTRY 6'-8" x 3'-6"
LAUNDRY 5'-4" x 6'-8"
PORCH 18'-7" x 12'-8"
WORK SHOP
TO OPTIONAL BONUS ROOM
LINE OF 5' HIGH KNEE WALL OF BONUS ROOM
BONUS ROOM 11'-8" x 21'-2"
GARAGE 23'-4" x 26'-8"

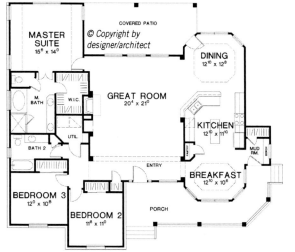

Images provided by designer/architect

PLAN #909-111D-0048

Dimensions: 56'6" W x 51'2" D
Heated Sq. Ft.: 1,972
Bedrooms: 3   Bathrooms: 2
Foundation: Slab standard; crawl space or basement for an additional fee

See index on page 104 for more information

Floor plan labels:
MASTER SUITE 15'⁶ x 14'⁰
COVERED PATIO
DINING 12'¹⁰ x 12'⁸
M. BATH
W.I.C.
GREAT ROOM 20'⁴ x 21'⁰
KITCHEN 12'¹⁰ x 11'¹⁰
BATH 2
UTIL.
MUD RM.
ENTRY
PANTRY
BREAKFAST 12'¹⁰ x 10'⁸
BEDROOM 3 12'⁰ x 10'⁸
BEDROOM 2 11'⁸ x 11'⁰
PORCH

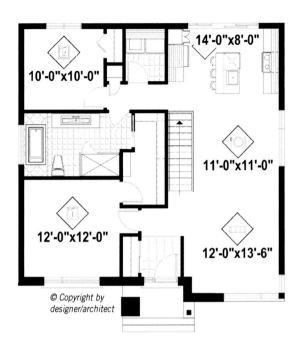

PLAN #909-126D-0517

Dimensions:	33' W x 34' D
Heated Sq. Ft.:	1,081
Bedrooms: 2	Bathrooms: 1
Exterior Walls:	2" x 6"
Foundation:	Basement

See index on page 104 for more information

Images provided by designer/architect

10'-0"x10'-0"

14'-0"x8'-0"

11'-0"x11'-0"

12'-0"x12'-0"

12'-0"x13'-6"

© Copyright by designer/architect

PLAN #909-144D-0013

Dimensions:	24' W x 36' D
Heated Sq. Ft.:	624
Bedrooms: 1	Bathrooms: 1
Exterior Walls:	2" x 6"
Foundation: Slab standard; crawl space for an additional fee	

See index on page 104 for more information

Images provided by designer/architect

PORCH

© Copyright by designer/architect

COATS

BRM.

MUDRM.
6' 0" x 12' 0"

BATH
6' 0" x 11' 6"

BEDROOM
10' 4" x 9' 4"

TOWELS

LIN.

CLOSET

PANTRY

KITCHEN
9' 7" x 13' 0"

SNACK BAR

LIVING ROOM
13' 6" x 13' 0"

DW

PORCH
15' 0" x 6' 0"

CALL 1-800-373-2646   **ONLINE** houseplansandmore.com

PLAN #909-091D-0507

Dimensions: 82'6" W x 69' D
Heated Sq. Ft.: 2,486
Bonus Sq. Ft.: 448
Bedrooms: 3   Bathrooms: 2½
Exterior Walls: 2" x 6"
Foundation: Basement or crawl space standard; slab for an additional fee
See index on page 104 for more information

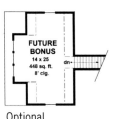

Optional
Second Floor
448 sq. ft.

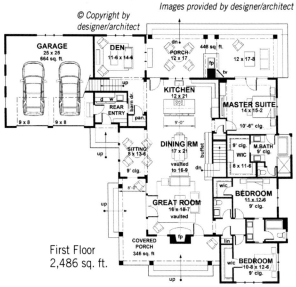

First Floor
2,486 sq. ft.

Images provided by designer/architect

PLAN #909-121D-0011

Images provided by designer/architect

Dimensions: 68'4" W x 56' D
Heated Sq. Ft.: 2,241
Bedrooms: 4   Bathrooms: 2½
Foundation: Basement standard; crawl space or slab for an additional fee
See index on page 104 for more information

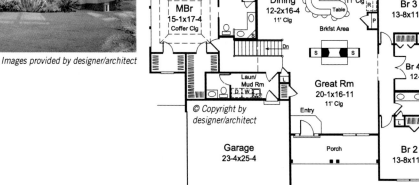
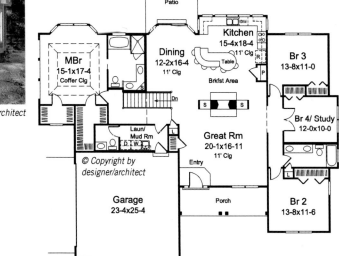

PLAN #909-005D-0001

Dimensions: 72' W x 34'4" D
Heated Sq. Ft.: 1,400
Bedrooms: 3 Bathrooms: 2
Foundation: Basement standard; crawl space or slab for an additional fee
See index on page 104 for more information

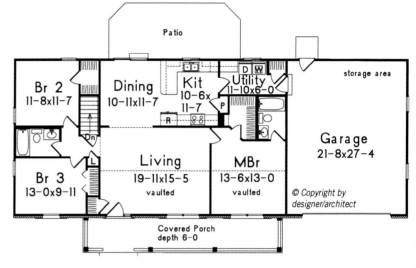

Patio

Br 2
11-8x11-7

Dining
10-11x11-7

Kit
10-6x
11-7

Utility
11-10x6-0

storage area

Dn

Br 3
13-0x9-11

Living
19-11x15-5
vaulted

MBr
13-6x13-0
vaulted

Garage
21-8x27-4

© Copyright by designer/architect

Covered Porch
depth 6-0

PLAN #909-077D-0019

Dimensions: 54' W x 47' D
Heated Sq. Ft.: 1,400
Bedrooms: 3 Bathrooms: 2
Foundation: Slab, basement or crawl space, please specify when ordering
See index on page 104 for more information

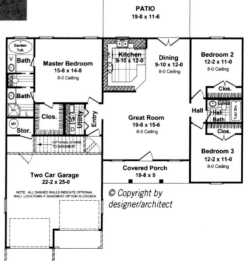

PATIO
19-8 x 11-6

Garden Tub

Bath

Bath

Master Bedroom
15-8 x 14-8
8-0 Ceiling

Kitchen
9-10 x 12-0

Dining
9-10 x 12-0
8-0 Ceiling

Bedroom 2
12-2 x 11-0
8-0 Ceiling

Clos.

Clos.

Utility

Entry

Hall

Bath

Stor.

Great Room
19-8 x 15-6
8-0 Ceiling

Clos.

Bedroom 3
12-2 x 11-0
8-0 Ceiling

OPTIONAL STAIRS TO BASEMENT

Two Car Garage
22-2 x 25-0

Covered Porch
19-8 x 5

NOTE: ALL DASHED WALLS INDICATE OPTIONAL WALL LOCATIONS IF BASEMENT OPTION IS CHOSEN

© Copyright by designer/architect

CALL 1-800-373-2646 **ONLINE** houseplansandmore.com

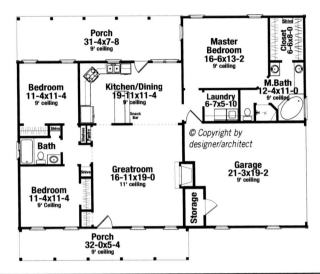

PLAN #909-084D-0016

Dimensions:	56' W x 45'8" D
Heated Sq. Ft.:	1,492
Bedrooms: 3	Bathrooms: 2

Foundation: Slab standard; basement or crawl space for an additional fee

See index on page 104 for more information

Porch
31-4x7-8
9' ceiling

Bedroom
11-4x11-4
9' ceiling

Kitchen/Dining
19-11x11-4
9' ceiling

Snack Bar

Master Bedroom
16-6x13-2
9' ceiling

Closet
6-9x8-0

M.Bath
12-4x11-0
9' ceiling

Laundry
6-7x5-10

Bath

Family

Shelves

Shlvs

Greatroom
16-11x19-0
11' ceiling

Bedroom
11-4x11-4
9' Ceiling

Storage

Garage
21-3x19-2
9' ceiling

© Copyright by designer/architect

Porch
32-0x5-4
9' ceiling

PLAN #909-013D-0217

Dimensions:	67'6" W x 46'4" D
Heated Sq. Ft.:	1,500
Bonus Sq. Ft.:	3,124
Bedrooms: 2	Bathrooms: 2½

Foundation: Basement standard; crawl space or slab for an additional fee

See index on page 104 for more information

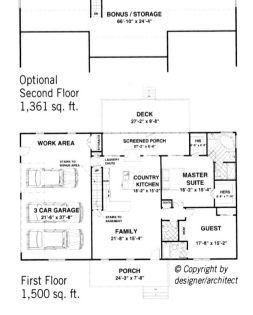

Optional Second Floor
1,361 sq. ft.

5' HIGH KNEE WALL
LINE OF 8' HIGH CEILING

DN

BONUS / STORAGE
66'-10" x 24'-4"

LAUNDRY
7'-4" x 6'-6"

BEDROOM 3
11'-4" x 13'-3"

BEDROOM 4
11'-4" x 13'-3"

POOL TABLE

FAMILY RECREATION
21'-8" x 22'-0"

HOME OFFICE
11'-3" x 14'-6"

EQUIPMENT STORAGE

HOME THEATER
27'-2" x 15'-0"

SNACK AREA

MECH.

EXERCISE AREA
11'-2" x 14'-10"

Optional Lower Level
1,763 sq. ft.

DECK
27'-2" x 9'-8"

WORK AREA

STORAGE

SCREENED PORCH
27'-2" x 6'-6"

HIS
6'-6" x 6'-6"

STAIRS TO BONUS AREA

UP

LAUNDRY CHUTE

COUNTRY KITCHEN
18'-2" x 15'-2"

MASTER SUITE
16'-2" x 15'-4"

3 CAR GARAGE
21'-6" x 37'-8"

STAIRS TO BASEMENT

COATS

HERS
6'-6" x 7'-10"

FAMILY
21'-8" x 15'-4"

GUEST
17'-8" x 15'-2"

DESK

PORCH
24'-3" x 7'-8"

© Copyright by designer/architect

First Floor
1,500 sq. ft.

PLAN #909-161D-0024

Dimensions: 114' W x 93'6" D
Heated Sq. Ft.:   3,665
Bedrooms: 3   Bathrooms: 3½
Exterior Walls: 2" x 6"
Foundation: Crawl space

See index on page 104 for more information

FEATURES

- Stunning modern sensibility offers limitless interior spaces and smart function in this beautiful home

- A great layout has two bedrooms in one wing, each with their own bath, and a game room tucked between them

- The kitchen is wide open to all activities in the great room and dining area

- The master suite enjoys a private spa courtyard, terrace access, a posh private bath, and massive walk-in closet

- Everyone will be jealous of the mud room which has a large bench with hooks, a powder room, a built-in desk and laundry access

- 3-car side entry garage

Images provided by designer/architect

© Copyright by designer/architect

PLAN #909-011D-0662

Dimensions: 76' W x 62' D
Heated Sq. Ft.: 2,460
Bedrooms: 3   Bathrooms: 2½
Exterior Walls: 2" x 6"
Foundation: Joisted continuous footings

See index on page 104 for more information

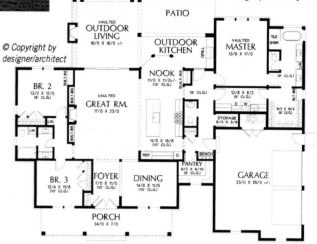

PLAN #909-121D-0023

Dimensions: 41' W x 60'4" D
Heated Sq. Ft.: 1,762
Bedrooms: 3   Bathrooms: 2
Foundation: Basement standard; crawl space or slab for an additional fee

See index on page 104 for more information

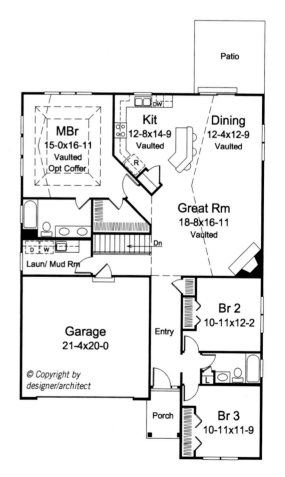

CALL 1-800-373-2646   **ONLINE** houseplansandmore.com

PLAN #909-028D-0109

Dimensions:	33' W x 40' D
Heated Sq. Ft.:	890
Bedrooms: 2	Bathrooms: 1
Exterior Walls:	2" x 6"

Foundation: Crawl space or slab, please specify when ordering

See index on page 104 for more information

PLAN #909-007D-0124

Dimensions:	65' W x 51' D
Heated Sq. Ft.:	1,944
Bedrooms: 3	Bathrooms: 2

Foundation: Basement standard; crawl space or slab for an additional fee

See index on page 104 for more information

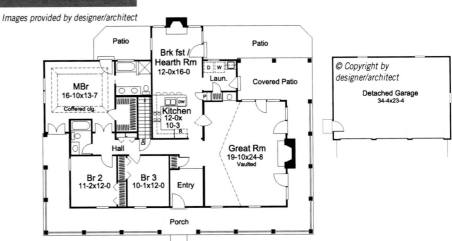

PLAN #909-101D-0056

Dimensions:	72' W x 77' D
Heated Sq. Ft.:	2,593
Bonus Sq. Ft.:	1,892
Bedrooms: 2	Bathrooms: 2½
Exterior Walls:	2" x 6"
Foundation:	Walk-out basement

See index on page 104 for more information

Images provided by designer/architect

FEATURES

- This stunning home has the look and feel homeowners love with its sleek interior and wide, open floor plan

- The great room, kitchen and dining area combine maximizing the square footage and making these spaces functional and comfortable

- The master bedroom enjoys a first floor private location adding convenience for the homeowners and it includes an oversized walk-in closet, and a private bath with a walk-in shower, a free-standing tub, and a double-bowl vanity

- The optional lower level has an additional 1,892 square feet of living area and adds extra amenities like a media area, a billiards room, a rec room, and an exercise room in addition to two additional bedrooms and two and a half baths

- 3-car front entry garage

First Floor
2,593 sq. ft.

© Copyright by designer/architect

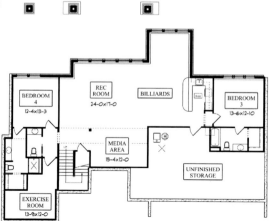

Optional
Lower Level
1,892 sq. ft.

CALL 1-800-373-2646   ONLINE houseplansandmore.com

PLAN #909-028D-0099

Dimensions:	30' W x 49' D
Heated Sq. Ft.:	1,320
Bedrooms: 3	Bathrooms: 2
Exterior Walls:	2" x 6"
Foundation:	Monolithic slab

See index on page 104 for more information

Images provided by designer/architect

FEATURES

- In a sensible size, this country home can easily incorporate some of the most popular Modern Farmhouse style trends into its floor plan
- The great room and kitchen/dining area blend together for seamless living that makes the interior feel larger than its true size
- Three bedrooms are located near each other for convenience
- A laundry room is centrally located adding ease with this frequent chore

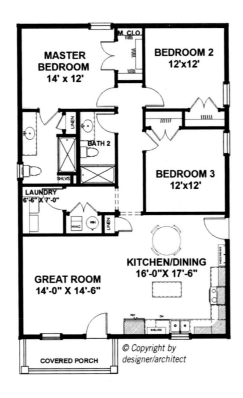

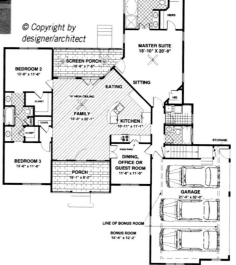

© Copyright by designer/architect

PLAN #909-013D-0156

Dimensions:	63' W x 73' D
Heated Sq. Ft.:	1,800
Bonus Sq. Ft.:	503
Bedrooms: 3	Bathrooms: 3

Foundation: Slab standard; basement or crawl space for an additional fee

See index on page 104 for more information

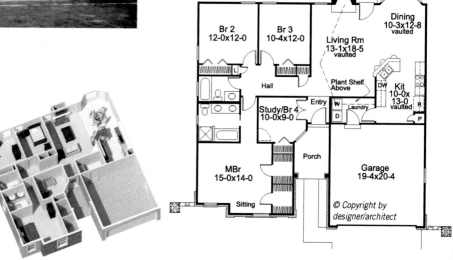

© Copyright by designer/architect

PLAN #909-007D-0162

Dimensions:	47'8" W x 47'4" D
Heated Sq. Ft.:	1,519
Bedrooms: 4	Bathrooms: 2

Foundation: Crawl space standard; basement or slab for an additional fee

See index on page 104 for more information

CALL 1-800-373-2646   **ONLINE** houseplansandmore.com

Images provided by designer/architect

PLAN #909-028D-0103

Dimensions:	40' W x 46' D
Heated Sq. Ft.:	1,520
Bedrooms: 2	Bathrooms: 1
Exterior Walls:	2" x 6"
Foundation:	Crawl space

See index on page 104 for more information

© Copyright by designer/architect

Images provided by designer/architect

PLAN #909-084D-0081

Dimensions:	62' W x 52'6" D
Heated Sq. Ft.:	1,631
Bedrooms: 3	Bathrooms: 2

Foundation: Slab standard; crawl space or basement for an additional fee

See index on page 104 for more information

© Copyright by designer/architect

PLAN #909-011D-0311

Dimensions:	64' W x 54' D
Heated Sq. Ft.:	1,988
Bedrooms: 3	Bathrooms: 3
Exterior Walls:	2" x 6"

Foundation: Joisted crawl space or post & beam standard; slab or basement for an additional fee

See index on page 104 for more information

Images provided by designer/architect

FEATURES

- So much function is packed into this floor plan including a small study with space for a computer, and a walk-in pantry with space designated for recycling
- The great room enjoys a fireplace and has a clear view of the kitchen
- The laundry room has a large built-in bench with cubbies for keeping everything organized on a daily basis
- A quiet guest room has its own bath for convenience
- 2-car front entry garage

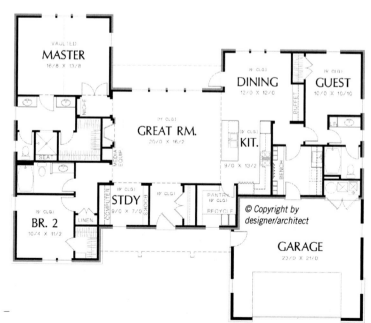

© Copyright by designer/architect

PLAN #909-055D-1039

Dimensions: 91'6" W x 61'3" D
Heated Sq. Ft.: 2,688
Bonus Sq. Ft.: 602
Bedrooms: 4 Bathrooms: 3½
Foundation: Crawl space or slab standard; basement or daylight basement for an additional fee
See index on page 104 for more information

FEATURES

- This stunning ranch home has a two-story vaulted and beamed ceiling in the great room and kitchen
- The outdoor living/grilling porch is adorned with a fireplace for extending your outdoor time into the colder months
- The master suite enjoys a private location and has a huge walk-in shower in the bath
- The optional second floor has an additional 602 square feet of living area
- 2-car side entry garage and a 1-car front entry garage

Images provided by designer/architect

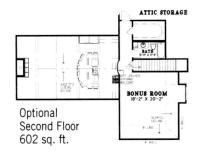

Optional
Second Floor
602 sq. ft.

© Copyright by
designer/architect

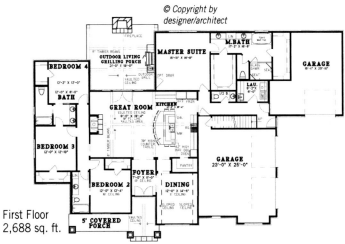

First Floor
2,688 sq. ft.

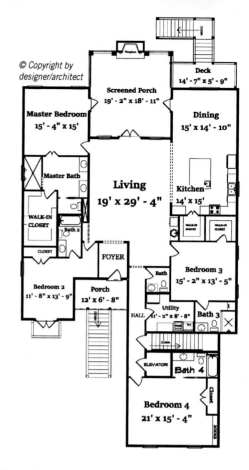

Images provided by designer/architect

PLAN #909-024D-0819

Dimensions: 51' W x 99'5" D
Heated Sq. Ft.:   2,530
Bedrooms: 4   Bathrooms: 4½
Exterior Walls: 2" x 6"
Foundation: Pilings
See index on page 104 for more information

Images provided by designer/architect

PLAN #909-077D-0138

Dimensions: 61' W x 47'4" D
Heated Sq. Ft.:   1,509
Bedrooms: 3   Bathrooms: 2
Foundation: Slab, basement or crawl space, please specify when ordering
See index on page 104 for more information

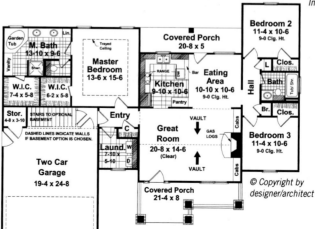

CALL 1-800-373-2646   **ONLINE** houseplansandmore.com

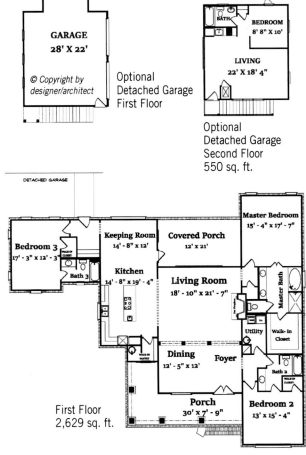

GARAGE
28' X 22'

© Copyright by designer/architect

Optional Detached Garage First Floor

BATH

BEDROOM
8' 8" X 10'

LIVING
22' X 18' 4"

Optional Detached Garage Second Floor 550 sq. ft.

DETACHED GARAGE

Bedroom 3
17' - 3" x 12' - 3"

Bath 3

Keeping Room
14' - 8" x 12'

Kitchen
14' - 8" x 19' - 4"

Covered Porch
12' x 21'

Living Room
18' - 10" x 21' - 7"

Master Bedroom
15' - 4" x 17' - 7"

Master Bath

Utility

Walk-in Closet

Dining
12' - 5" x 12'

Foyer

Bath 2

Walk-in Closet

First Floor
2,629 sq. ft.

Porch
30' x 7' - 9"

Bedroom 2
13' x 15' - 4"

Images provided by designer/architect

PLAN #909-024D-0820

Dimensions:	76' W x 100' D
Heated Sq. Ft.:	2,629
Bonus Sq. Ft.:	550
Bedrooms: 3	Bathrooms: 3
Foundation:	Floating slab

See index on page 104 for more information

Images provided by designer/architect

PATIO
14'-0" X 10'-0"

GARAGE
13'-0" X 20'-0"

KIT.
9'-0" X 11'-8"

BED RM. 2
9'-4" X 11'-4"

BED RM. 3
12'-0" X 9'-0"

BATH

© Copyright by designer/architect

GREAT ROOM
14'-2" X 18'-8"

MASTER BEDROOM
13'-4" X 12'-6"

M.B.

PLAN #909-155D-0171

Dimensions:	53'8" W x 41'4" D
Heated Sq. Ft.:	1,131
Bedrooms: 3	Bathrooms: 2

Foundation: Crawl space or slab, please specify when ordering

See index on page 104 for more information

PLAN #909-051D-0960

Dimensions: 117' W x 50'8" D
Heated Sq. Ft.: 2,784
Bedrooms: 3   Bathrooms: 2
Exterior Walls: 2" x 6"
Foundation: Basement standard; crawl space or slab for an additional fee

See index on page 104 for more information

Images provided by designer/architect

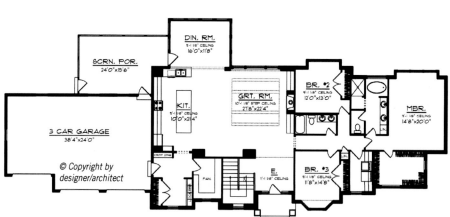

FEATURES

- This Traditional ranch home design is sure to win you over with a very classy exterior
- You are welcomed into the home with eleven-foot ceilings in the entry
- All three bedrooms, including the master bedroom, are located to right in the house
- The master bedroom includes a bath with a spa style tub, and dual sinks, as well as a spacious walk-in closet
- The other two bedrooms share a full bath nearby
- The three-stall garage is located on the left side of the house with a large screened-in porch behind it
- 3-car front entry garage

PLAN #909-101D-0094

Dimensions:	72' W x 72'9" D
Heated Sq. Ft.:	2,650
Bonus Sq. Ft.:	1,821
Bedrooms: 3	Bathrooms: 2½
Exterior Walls:	2" x 6"
Foundation:	Basement

See index on page 104 for more information

Images provided by designer/architect

FEATURES

- Sleek Prairie-inspired exterior is refreshing and uncomplicated creating great curb appeal
- The dining, kitchen and great room combine creating a large informal gathering space for family and friends
- U-shaped layout and curved breakfast bar highlight the kitchen
- Located right off the garage is a mud room, laundry room and pantry
- With double walk-in closets, a luxurious bath complete with a free-standing tub and see-through fireplace, this master suite is the perfect retreat
- The optional lower level has an additional 1,821 square feet of living area and includes a large recreation room with a wet bar, two additional bedrooms and a full bath, plus a wine room
- 3-car front entry garage

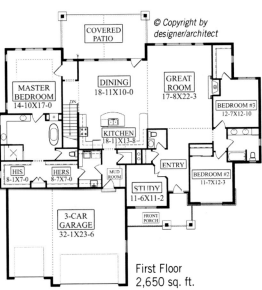

First Floor
2,650 sq. ft.

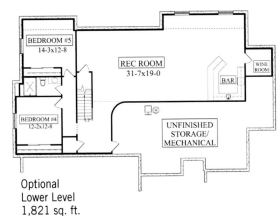

Optional
Lower Level
1,821 sq. ft.

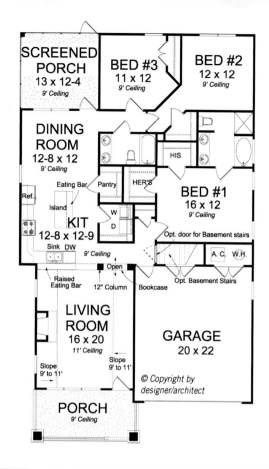

PLAN #909-130D-0394

Dimensions: 39' W x 66' D
Heated Sq. Ft.: 1,581
Bedrooms: 3   Bathrooms: 2
Foundation: Slab standard; basement or crawl space for an additional fee
See index on page 104 for more information

SCREENED PORCH 13 x 12-4 9' Ceiling
BED #3 11 x 12 9' Ceiling
BED #2 12 x 12 9' Ceiling
DINING ROOM 12-8 x 12 9' Ceiling
HIS
HER'S
BED #1 16 x 12 9' Ceiling
Ref.
Eating Bar
Pantry
Island
W D
KIT 12-8 x 12-9
Sink   DW
9' Ceiling
Open
Opt. door for Basement stairs
A.C.   W.H.
Raised Eating Bar
12" Column
Bookcase
Opt. Basement Stairs
LIVING ROOM 16 x 20 11' Ceiling
GARAGE 20 x 22
Slope 9' to 11'
Slope 9' to 11'
PORCH 9' Ceiling

PLAN #909-011D-0640

Dimensions: 58' W x 62' D
Heated Sq. Ft.: 1,834
Bedrooms: 3   Bathrooms: 2
Exterior Walls: 2" x 6"
Foundation: Joisted crawl space standard; slab or basement for an additional fee
See index on page 104 for more information

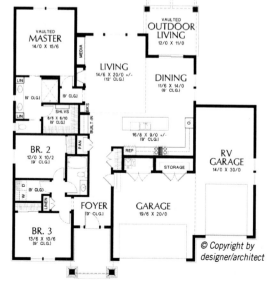

VAULTED **MASTER** 14/0 X 15/6
MEDIA
VAULTED **OUTDOOR LIVING** 12/0 X 11/0
LIVING 14/6 X 20/0 +/- (12' CLG.)
DINING 11/6 X 14/0 (9' CLG.)
LIN
LIN
LIN
SHLVS 8/6 X 6/10 (8' CLG.)
BUILT-IN
BKS
16/8 X 9/0 (9' CLG.)
BR. 2 12/0 X 10/2 (9' CLG.)
PAN
REF
STORAGE
RV GARAGE 14/0 X 30/0
D
W
LINEN
BR. 3 13/6 X 10/6 (9' CLG.)
FOYER (9' CLG.)
GARAGE 19/6 X 20/0

CALL 1-800-373-2646   ONLINE houseplansandmore.com

Optional
Second Floor
591 sq. ft.

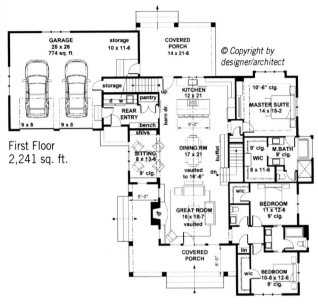

First Floor
2,241 sq. ft.

© Copyright by
designer/architect

Images provided by designer/architect

PLAN #909-091D-0506

Dimensions:	82' W x 71' D
Heated Sq. Ft.:	2,241
Bonus Sq. Ft.:	591
Bedrooms: 3	Bathrooms: 2½
Exterior Walls:	2" x 6"

Foundation: Crawl space or basement
standard; daylight basement or
walk-out basement for an additional
fee

See index on page 104 for more information

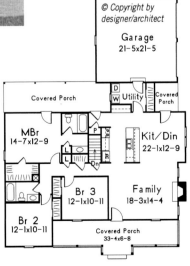

© Copyright by
designer/architect

Images provided by designer/architect

PLAN #909-001D-0031

Dimensions:	48' W x 66' D
Heated Sq. Ft.:	1,501
Bedrooms: 3	Bathrooms: 2

Foundation: Basement standard;
crawl space or slab for an additional
fee

See index on page 104 for more information

great home designs for
ENTERTAINING

Most of the year, homeowners tend to entertain smaller groups of family or friends, so owning a modest-sized home can handle these get-togethers without a hitch. But, one thing that can make a smaller-sized home, or a one-story home instantly shrink is when a larger get-together is in order. Whether it's the holidays, or a special occasion with cause for a celebration such as a graduation or special anniversary, sometimes a one-story home, or a smaller home that is ideal for your daily life feels like it can't possibly offer a comfortable environment for all the party-goers.

Whether you're just starting out, or you've downsized, the last thing you want to do is have a home where you can't invite family to stay in comfort, or throw an event without everyone feeling cramped. After all, this is what life is all about - being able to spend time with those you care about and create memories with them! It is possible to build a home that isn't huge in size, but offers comfortable solutions when guests stay, or parties are thrown. There are certain types of one-story homes or floor plans that are better suited for these types of situations.

split decision

Even if you want to build a one-story home, there are ways to give visitors, as well as yourself, the privacy everyone truly deserves. Consider choosing a split bedroom floor plan that has the master suite placed in a different location of the home than the other bedrooms. Currently, this is one of the most popular floor plan layouts for many homeowners. It is great when guests are visiting because everyone has their own privacy and space, but it is also ideal if you have teenagers or a live-in parent, because everyone will appreciate their own area to retreat to.

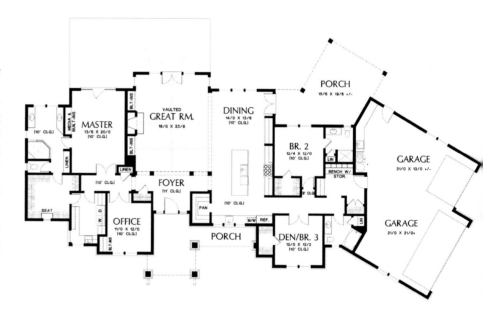

be open

Home designs with both formal and informal dining areas, and house plans with open floor plans and only one dining space are popular for different reasons. Having a home with both formal and informal dining areas may allow for more intimate dining situations, perhaps with the adults in the formal setting and the kids in the casual one. Instead of the moms and dads constantly tending to the kids at the same table, create the popular "kid's table," and let them fend for themselves during the meal. More often than not, the older kids chip in and help the little ones handle their utensils and cut their food. It will make the adult's dining experience more enjoyable. Although becoming less popular in recent years with the popularity of the open floor plan style, many homes still offer both a formal and informal space and many homeowners still appreciate multiple dining options especially if they like to entertain formally as well as casually and do both often.

But, with the open-concept floor plan becoming increasingly popular, this layout typically offers only one designated dining area within a larger space that often includes the kitchen as well as the great room. A home with an open floor plan typically has one large space where dining, cooking, and relaxing all take place. It's a great layout for keeping those in the kitchen in the loop to all of the fun going on in the great room, while also keeping the dining table easily accessible when serving and cleaning up. This layout has become increasingly popular as the average home size has decreased. Removing interior walls creates the sense of a larger home since the absence of walls actually maximizes square footage. It's really important when looking at house plans to pay attention to the amount of space you'll have when entertaining, and that includes the amount of dining areas. If the floor plan only includes one space for dining, then often the kitchen features an island with built-in casual dining space. It's typically close to the space designated for a dining table, so it can offer that additional seating needed with larger crowds. This space, can be a fun option for the kids, too.

double your pleasure

As your family expands in size, and your own children marry and have children, you will realize your one-story home may start to bust at the seams when everyone gathers for family events and celebrations. A wise consideration is to double your square footage, or come close to it by finishing your basement. By creating an additional space for entertaining, dining, or just hanging out, a finished lower level is full of possibilities that can include a wet bar, dining space with high-top tables, billiards, a game room, an exercise room, a wine cellar, or even a home theater. As soon as the kids come in the house, you know where they'll head to and that will leave the grown-ups with some much-needed down-time.

step outside

If you have a modest-sized home, but need extra space for fami barbecues and other holiday get-togethers, then choosing a floor plan with an outdoor living space will make your home feel much larger than its true size. Choose an outdoor space that has a cov ered porch and the space becomes even more functional since can now handle inclement weather. Screen it in, and It will make pest-free dining space. Add comfy furniture, a fire pit, an outdoo fireplace, or maybe even an outdoor bar, kitchen or pizza over and now you've created a spot that allows guests to enjoy th outdoors in total comfort. You can entertain easily and possib even cook the meal for your get-together right in the same place Homeowners now more than ever are relishing in the time they ca spend in nature and creating a backyard oasis will provide tha special place to relax, unwind, and regroup.

be our guest

Some other home design ideas include choosing a home plan wit a mother-in-law suite, a guest house, a free-standing apartmen garage, or a multi-family plan. All of these options take privacy t a different level when housing guests. Most home designs with guest house are high-end luxury homes, often very large in size So, why is a guest house even needed then? Well, it's a great wa to offer guests plenty of privacy away from the noise of the mai home. Or, perhaps you need an in-law suite and want it to b handicap accessible. A small dwelling away from the main home similar to a "granny pod," provides a comfortable, quiet, and eas ily accessible space for people of all ages and physical abilities. I also provides a place where they can independently live on thei own with dignity. If you're in the market for a luxury home, con sider a home with a guest house. Family and friends will be glad you did! But, if you plan to build something much smaller tha a large luxury home, then consider a lot that offers enough spac that it can handle a guest house. Not only great for guests, or live-in parent, it can also provide rental income when not in us by family or friends.

a separate hideaway

Apartment garage plans have really come a long way in recent years and are definitely growing in popularity as the general population continues to age and multi-generational housing options are becoming more popular. This is a great option if you already have a home you love, but need additional garage and living space, An apartment garage is great for the live-in college student too. Typically, these dwellings offer a small studio apartment above the garage, creating the perfect private and affordable little place to live.

seeing double

If you want or need to be close to family, but also want everyone to have their own designated space, then a multi-family plan may be the right choice. Think of it as two separate houses that share one wall. Everyone will be in close proximity to each another, but each family member has their own residence. It's quite possibly the best of both worlds!

As family and friends descend on your usually ideal-sized home, think about how your future home could better handle all of those frequently visiting relatives with some of these different housing choices and floor plan options. Instead of it being stressful when visitors arrive, these ideas and design options will make visits comfortable and memorable in all the right ways.

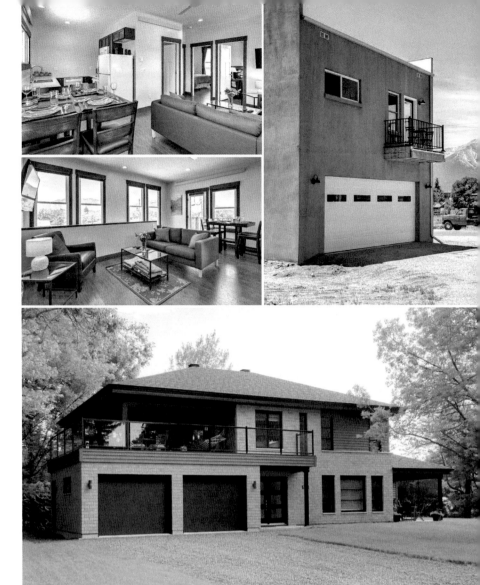

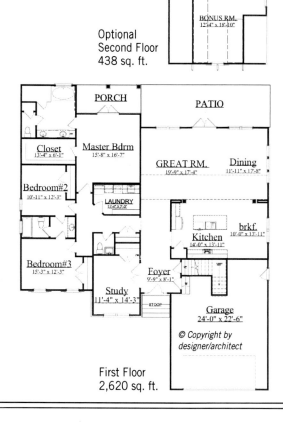

PLAN #909-157D-0015

Dimensions: 62' W x 74'4" D
Heated Sq. Ft.:   2,620
Bonus Sq. Ft.:   438
Bedrooms: 3   Bathrooms: 2½
Foundation: Crawl space standard;
slab for an additional fee
See index on page 104 for more information

Optional
Second Floor
438 sq. ft.

First Floor
2,620 sq. ft.

PLAN #909-141D-0294

Dimensions: 74' W x 66' D
Heated Sq. Ft.:   2,491
Bedrooms: 3   Bathrooms: 2½
Foundation: Slab or crawl space,
please specify when ordering
See index on page 104 for more information

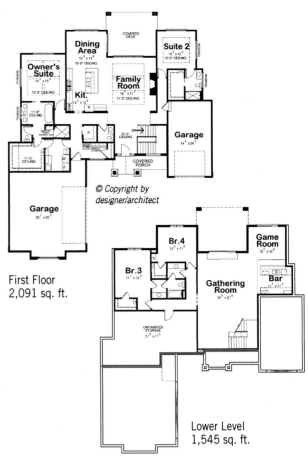

Images provided by designer/architect

© Copyright by designer/architect

First Floor
2,091 sq. ft.

Lower Level
1,545 sq. ft.

PLAN #909-026D-2106

Dimensions: 67'4" W x 78'8" D
Heated Sq. Ft.:   3,636
Bedrooms: 4   Bathrooms: 3½
Exterior Walls: 2" x 6"
Foundation: Basement standard;
slab, crawl space or walk-out
basement for an additional fee

See index on page 104 for more information

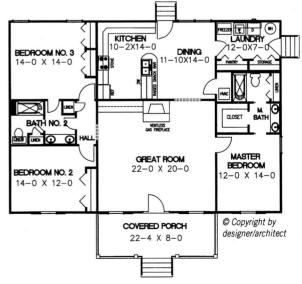

Images provided by designer/architect

© Copyright by designer/architect

PLAN #909-028D-0006

Dimensions: 50' W x 42' D
Heated Sq. Ft.:   1,700
Bedrooms: 3   Bathrooms: 2
Foundation: Crawl space, basement
or slab, please specify when ordering

See index on page 104 for more information

PLAN #909-007D-0113

Images provided by designer/architect

Dimensions: 66' W x 66' D
Heated Sq. Ft.:   2,547
Bedrooms: 4   Bathrooms: 2½
Foundation: Basement
See index on page 104 for more information

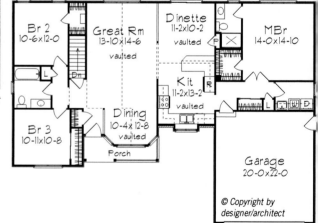

PLAN #909-033D-0012

Images provided by designer/architect

Dimensions: 60' W x 43' D
Heated Sq. Ft.:   1,546
Bedrooms: 3   Bathrooms: 2
Foundation: Basement
See index on page 104 for more information

PLAN #909-011D-0660

Dimensions: 52' W x 53' D
Heated Sq. Ft.: 1,704
Bedrooms: 3   Bathrooms: 2½
Exterior Walls: 2" x 6"
Foundation: Joisted continuous footings or post & beam standard; slab for an additional fee

See index on page 104 for more information

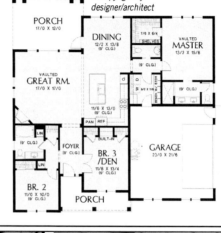

PLAN #909-056S-0007

Dimensions: 117'6" W x 82'2" D
Heated Sq. Ft.: 3,954
Bonus Sq. Ft.: 3,954
Bedrooms: 4   Bathrooms: 4½
Foundation: Basement standard; crawl space or slab for an additional fee

See index on page 104 for more information

Optional Lower Level
3,954 sq. ft.

First Floor
3,954 sq. ft.

PLAN #909-101D-0045

Dimensions:	69' W x 68'3" D
Heated Sq. Ft.:	1,885
Bedrooms: 2	Bathrooms: 2½
Exterior Walls:	2" x 6"
Foundation:	Basement

See index on page 104 for more information

Images provided by designer/architect

FEATURES

- The open floor plan maximizes space creating an open flowing layout
- A dual fireplace warms the family room as well as the outdoor covered patio
- The spacious and private master suite includes its own bath and sizable walk-in closet
- Guests will never want to leave the guest bedroom with its own bath and large walk-in closet
- 3-car front entry garage

PLAN #909-028D-0093

Dimensions: 34' W x 62'3" D
Heated Sq. Ft.: 1,567
Bedrooms: 3   Bathrooms: 2
Exterior Walls: 2" x 6"
Foundation: Slab or crawl space,
please specify when ordering
See index on page 104 for more information

Images provided by designer/architect

FEATURES

- Quaint bungalow farmhouse touches create an inviting friendly feel to this Craftsman bungalow
- The great room enjoys a cozy fireplace and has direct access into the kitchen
- The kitchen enjoys a handy laundry room nearby, plenty of dining space, an island for prepping meals and a mud room entrance with a built-in bench
- The bedrooms all have privacy in their own hall away from the main gathering spaces
- A covered front porch, a rear covered porch and a screened porch all provide great opportunities to enjoy the outdoors

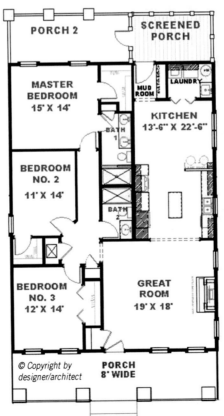

PORCH 2

SCREENED PORCH

MASTER BEDROOM
15' X 14'

MUD ROOM

LAUNDRY

KITCHEN
13'-6" X 22'-6"

BATH 1

BEDROOM NO. 2
11' X 14'

BATH 2

BEDROOM NO. 3
12' X 14'

GREAT ROOM
19' X 18'

© Copyright by designer/architect

PORCH 8' WIDE

PLAN #909-121D-0016

Dimensions: 42'4" W x 54' D
Heated Sq. Ft.:   1,582
Bedrooms: 3   Bathrooms: 2
Foundation: Basement standard; crawl space or slab for an additional fee

See index on page 104 for more information

Detached Garage
23-4x23-4

© Copyright by designer/architect

PLAN #909-051D-0696

Dimensions: 84'8" W x 50' D
Heated Sq. Ft.:   2,016
Bonus Sq. Ft.:   453
Bedrooms: 3   Bathrooms: 2
Exterior Walls: 2" x 6"
Foundation: Basement standard; crawl space or slab for an additional fee

See index on page 104 for more information

First Floor
2,016 sq. ft.

© Copyright by designer/architect

Optional
Second Floor
453 sq. ft.

CALL 1-800-373-2646   **ONLINE** houseplansandmore.com

PLAN #909-144D-0023

Dimensions: 58' W x 32' D
Heated Sq. Ft.: 928
Bedrooms: 2   Bathrooms: 2
Exterior Walls: 2" x 6"
Foundation: Crawl space or slab standard; basement or daylight basement for an additional fee
See index on page 104 for more information

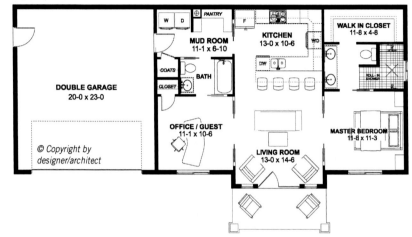

DOUBLE GARAGE
20-0 x 23-0

MUD ROOM
11-1 x 6-10

KITCHEN
13-0 x 10-6

WALK IN CLOSET
11-8 x 4-8

BATH

OFFICE / GUEST
11-1 x 10-6

LIVING ROOM
13-0 x 14-6

MASTER BEDROOM
11-8 x 11-3

© Copyright by designer/architect

PLAN #909-007D-0146

Images provided by designer/architect

Dimensions: 68' W x 49'8" D
Heated Sq. Ft.: 1,929
Bedrooms: 4   Bathrooms: 3
Foundation: Crawl space standard; slab or basement for an additional fee
See index on page 104 for more information

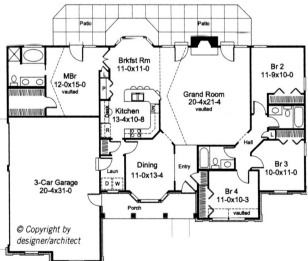

Patio

Patio

MBr
12-0x15-0
vaulted

Brkfst Rm
11-0x11-0

Grand Room
20-4x21-4
vaulted

Br 2
11-9x10-0

Kitchen
13-4x10-8

Hall

Dining
11-0x13-4

Entry

Br 3
10-0x11-0

3-Car Garage
20-4x31-0

Laun

Br 4
11-0x10-3
vaulted

Porch

© Copyright by designer/architect

PLAN #909-026D-1890

Dimensions: 69' W x 68' D
Heated Sq. Ft.: 2,449
Bedrooms: 3 Bathrooms: 2½
Foundation: Slab standard; basement or crawl space for an additional fee
See index on page 104 for more information

FEATURES

- The spacious great room with fireplace combines seamlessly with the kitchen and dining area
- Double doors lead to a den, perfect as a private office
- The mud room has great organization with lockers and benches making it a great drop zone
- The kitchen features an angled island overlooking the great room, another prep island, a huge walk-in pantry, and covered porch access
- The master bedroom has a large bath and walk-in closet
- 2-car side entry garage, and an optional 1-car front entry garage

First Floor
2,449 sq. ft.

Optional Stairs

© Copyright by designer/architect

Images provided by designer/architect

PLAN #909-101D-0059

Dimensions: 88'6" W x 67'6" D
Heated Sq. Ft.: 2,196
Bonus Sq. Ft.: 1,517
Bedrooms: 2   Bathrooms: 2
Exterior Walls: 2" x 6"
Foundation: Basement, daylight basement or walk-out basement, please specify when ordering
See index on page 104 for more information

Images provided by designer/architect

FEATURES

- This home was designed with 10' ceilings on both the first floor and the lower level making it extremely open and spacious

- The laundry and mud room merge to form a powerhouse of efficiency and organization including lockers, a closet, and extra counter space

- The L-shaped kitchen island offers plenty of seating and houses a double sink and the dishwasher

- The optional lower level has an additional 1,517 square feet of living area

- 2-car front entry, 1-car side entry garage

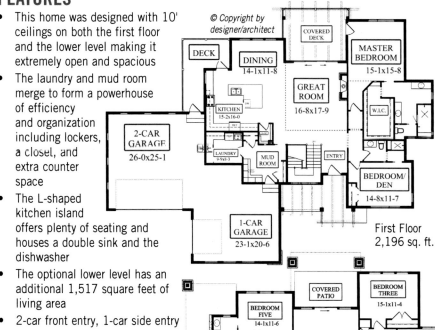

© Copyright by designer/architect

First Floor
2,196 sq. ft.

DECK
DINING 14-1x11-8
COVERED DECK
MASTER BEDROOM 15-1x15-8
KITCHEN 15-2x16-0
GREAT ROOM 16-8x17-9
W.I.C.
2-CAR GARAGE 26-0x25-1
LAUNDRY 9-9x8-3
MUD ROOM
ENTRY
1-CAR GARAGE 23-1x20-6
BEDROOM/ DEN 14-8x11-7

Optional Lower Level
1,517 sq. ft.

COVERED PATIO
BEDROOM THREE 15-1x11-4
BEDROOM FIVE 14-1x11-6
REC. AREA 16-10x21-10
BEDROOM FOUR 12-3x13-8
EXERCISE ROOM 12-10x15-9
UNFINISHED STORAGE
UNFINISHED STORAGE

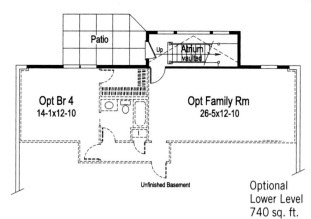

**Optional
Lower Level
740 sq. ft.**

Patio

Up

Atrium
vaulted

Opt Br 4
14-1x12-10

Opt Family Rm
26-5x12-10

Unfinished Basement

PLAN #909-007D-0136

Dimensions:	71'8" W x 38' D
Heated Sq. Ft.:	1,532
Bonus Sq. Ft.:	740
Bedrooms: 3	Bathrooms: 2
Foundation:	Walk-out basement

See index on page 104 for more information

Images provided by designer/architect

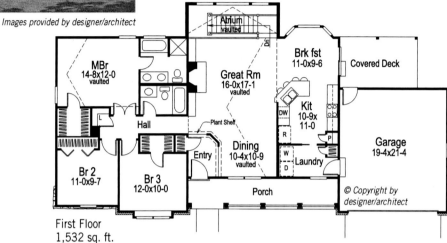

Atrium
vaulted

MBr
14-8x12-0
vaulted

Great Rm
16-0x17-1
vaulted

Brk fst
11-0x9-6

Covered Deck

Hall

Plant Shelf

Kit
10-9x
11-0

DW

R

Garage
19-4x21-4

Dining
10-4x10-9
vaulted

Entry

Laundry

W
D

P

Br 2
11-0x9-7

Br 3
12-0x10-0

Porch

© Copyright by
designer/architect

**First Floor
1,532 sq. ft.**

PLAN #909-034D-0119

Dimensions:	49'8" W x 58' D
Heated Sq. Ft.:	1,986
Bedrooms: 3	Bathrooms: 2
Foundation:	Basement

See index on page 104 for more information

Images provided by designer/architect

**Covered Porch
Option Included**

DIN

Optional Covered Porch
20'8 x 12'

MBR

GREAT RM

DIN
14'4 x 13'
tray cl'g

KIT
tray cl'g
14'4 x 13'

GREAT RM
18'8 x 18'4

MBR
15'4 x 16'4
plus bay
tray cl'g

REF

ARCHWAY

WIC

MBATH

Laundry

Entry

ARCHWAY

LINEN

TWO-CAR GARAGE
21' x 21'8

FOYER

STUDY /
BR3
10' x 10'4

WIC

BATH2

LINEN

BR2
12'2 x 11'4

Covered Porch

© Copyright by
designer/architect

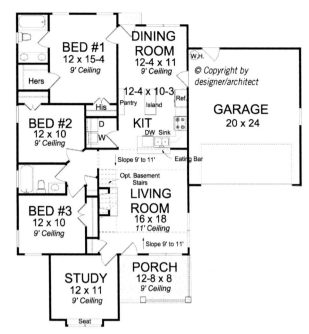

Images provided by designer/architect

PLAN #909-130D-0395

Dimensions: 51' W x 54'4" D
Heated Sq. Ft.: 1,420
Bedrooms: 3   Bathrooms: 2
Foundation: Slab standard; basement
or crawl space for an additional fee
See index on page 104 for more information

Images provided by designer/architect

PLAN #909-141D-0297

Dimensions: 37'6" W x 74'3" D
Heated Sq. Ft.: 2,168
Bedrooms: 3   Bathrooms: 2
Foundation: Crawl space
See index on page 104 for more information

PLAN #909-011D-0342

Dimensions: 63' W x 61'6" D
Heated Sq. Ft.: 2,368
Bedrooms: 3   Bathrooms: 2½
Exterior Walls: 2" x 6"
Foundation: Joisted crawl space or post & beam standard; slab or basement for an additional fee
See index on page 104 for more information

Images provided by designer/architect

FEATURES

- This Craftsman home's curb appeal will make it a standout in any neighborhood with its tasteful combination of stone, siding and multiple gables
- The chef of the family will love the island in the kitchen, the walk-in pantry, and the spacious snack bar space
- The laundry room is bright and cheerful, with plenty of counterspace for folding clothes
- The secluded office could serve as a guest room, or a place for hobbies
- The well-appointed master suite features a vaulted ceiling, and a lovely window arrangement with transoms above that overlooks the backyard
- A sit-down shower anchors the posh master bath, which also includes a toilet space, dual sinks and a walk-in closet
- 3-car front entry garage

PLAN #909-076D-0280

Dimensions: 61'8" W x 78'4" D
Heated Sq. Ft.: 2,585
Bonus Sq. Ft.: 492
Bedrooms: 4   Bathrooms: 3½
Foundation: Crawl space or slab, please specify when ordering
See index on page 104 for more information

Images provided by designer/architect

FEATURES

- This stunning Craftsman inspired home has a coveted split bedroom open floor plan for maintaining a sense of spaciousness and privacy
- All bedrooms have generous walk-in closets
- A vaulted covered terrace creates the perfect spot to relax outdoors
- Upon entering this home you will find an open floor plan concept for the dining room, family room and kitchen
- The second floor has an additional 492 square feet of living area in the bonus room
- 2-car side entry garage

Second Floor
355 sq. ft.

First Floor
2,230 sq. ft.

© Copyright by designer/architect

PLAN #909-007D-0140

Dimensions: 62' W x 45' D
Heated Sq. Ft.: 1,591
Bedrooms: 3   Bathrooms: 2
Foundation: Basement standard;
crawl space or slab for an additional
fee

See index on page 104 for more information

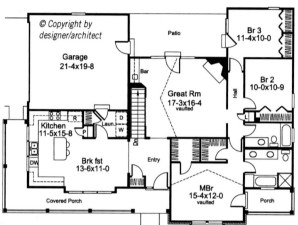

PLAN #909-013D-0226

Dimensions: 53'8" W x 60'1" D
Heated Sq. Ft.: 1,800
Bonus Sq. Ft.: 2,223
Bedrooms: 3   Bathrooms: 2½
Foundation: Basement standard;
crawl space or slab for an additional
fee

See index on page 104 for more information

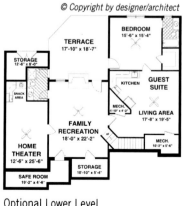

Optional Lower Level
1,900 sq. ft.

First Floor
1,800 sq. ft.

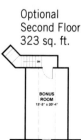

Optional
Second Floor
323 sq. ft.

CALL 1-800-373-2646   **ONLINE** houseplansandmore.com

PLAN #909-084D-0087

Dimensions: 78' W x 80' D
Heated Sq. Ft.: 3,507
Bonus Sq. Ft:. 716
Bedrooms: 4 Bathrooms: 3
Foundation: Slab standard; crawl space or basement for an additional fee

See index on page 104 for more information

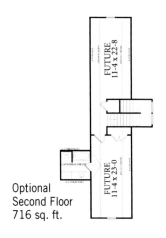

FUTURE
11-4 x 22-8

FUTURE
11-4 x 23-0

Optional
Second Floor
716 sq. ft.

MASTER
BEDROOM
17-4 x 21-4
10' CLG.

OUTDOOR
ROOM
18-8 x 19-10
10' CLG.

OUTDOOR
KITCHEN
22-8 x 11-2
10' CLG.

BEDROOM
11-4 x 12-0
10' CLG.

BATH

M. BATH
13-2 x 12-4
10' CLG.

DINING
15-10 x 12-8
10' CLG.

LAUNDRY
11-8 x 8-4

STOR.
ROOM
7-2 x 8-4

CLOSET
17-4 x 9-0
10' CLG.

LIVING
19-6 x 23-4
12' CLG.

KITCHEN
15-10 x 19-4

MUD
ROOM

BEDROOM
13-4 x 11-8
10' CLG.

GARAGE
23-4 x 27-0
9' CLG.

BEDROOM
12-0 x 13-4
12' CLG.

FOYER
7-4 x 13-8

DINING
12-0 x 13-4
12' CLG.

PANTRY
7-10 x 11-4

BATH

PORCH
33-8 x 10-4
12' CLG.

© Copyright by
designer/architect

First Floor
3,507 sq. ft.

PLAN #909-121D-0031

Dimensions: 46' W x 36' D
Heated Sq. Ft.: 1,308
Bedrooms: 3 Bathrooms: 2
Foundation: Basement standard; crawl space or slab for an additional fee

See index on page 104 for more information

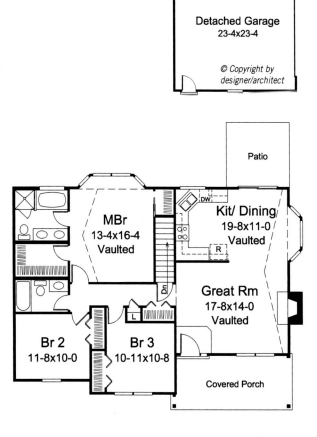

Detached Garage
23-4x23-4

© Copyright by
designer/architect

Patio

MBr
13-4x16-4
Vaulted

Kit/ Dining
19-8x11-0
Vaulted

Great Rm
17-8x14-0
Vaulted

Br 2
11-8x10-0

Br 3
10-11x10-8

Covered Porch

eat, play & live:
using your
OUTDOOR SPACE

A buzzword surrounding home construction in recent years is "outdoor living," and it is definitely a trend that is here to stay.

For many homeowners the opportunity to have a backyard paradise is too good to pass up. However, thoughts of swimming pools, gardens, outdoor televisions, fireplaces, stonework, bars, kitchen centers, fabrics, and furniture swirl through the mind, creating overwhelming confusion. Sure, outdoor living space is great, but beyond the grill, where do you even start? How extensive is this project going to be?

The first thing to remember about outdoor living is that it can be made as simple or as grand as you desire. Starting with a set budget will help determine what outdoor living components can become a reality. The second task is to evaluate the space. A small patio can be ideal for hosting dinner parties with friends and family, but the dream of a swimming pool and private garden is likely out of scope. Will it be better to have one multi-purpose area or designated zones for dining, resting, and play? Take note of the space available and determine which amenities are most important to your lifestyle. These ideas will help get you started on creating your perfect outdoor oasis designed to complement your home and provide a place of tranquility.

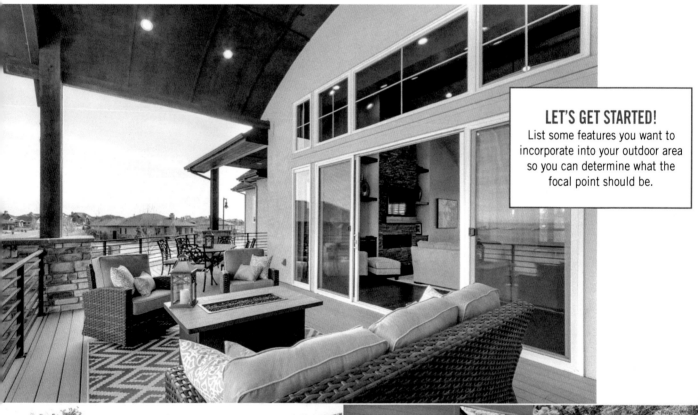

LET'S GET STARTED!
List some features you want to incorporate into your outdoor area so you can determine what the focal point should be.

the outdoor kitchen

By far, the most popular component of outdoor living spaces is the outdoor kitchen. People tend to naturally gather in the kitchen, so this combines the work of hosting with the pleasure of visiting guests. To ensure a truly functional space, it is important to look at how the outdoor kitchen will be used in your life. A basic outdoor kitchen is an extension of the home and typically contains a small prep sink, grill, and limited counter space for small tasks. Close proximity to the indoor kitchen allows easy transport of ingredients, dishes, and drinks not accessible in the outdoor kitchen. On the other end of the spectrum, an outdoor kitchen can be fully independent from the home, complete with a dishwasher, refrigerator, cook top, with ample storage provided. These elaborate kitchens are ideal for hosting large groups and are typically L-shaped or U-shaped with an island, creating a work atmosphere with distinct zones for food preparation and cooking. Outdoor kitchens of any size can be fully built-in with massive grills, or they can be comprised of rolling carts that move when necessary. The option of permanent versus flexible is often determined by budget and local climate. Also gaining in popularity and an extension of the outdoor kitchen idea is an outdoor bar. Typically less expensive, it's a designated hang-out spot for mixing up your favorite libations among friends.

the outdoor social space

Though the outdoor kitchen is incredibly popular, the need for a place to retreat to cannot be ignored. The options are endless when it comes to creating a space that is perfect for private or social use. Again, determined by budget and need, outdoor living rooms can be sprawling extensions of the indoors, full of cozy couches and chairs, fireplaces, and even outdoor media centers. There can be separate dining and resting spaces, or these can be combined into one multi-purpose space with a few well-chosen pieces of furniture. The choice is up to you, but either option can be a haven of comfort.

outdoor play spaces

While outdoor living is ideal for creating paradise close to home, the outdoors is still a place of fun. While designating space for dining and resting, keep in mind the need for play space. Some outdoor living spaces use hedges and landscaping to create play areas in the yard. Not only are these dividers decorative, they keep errant balls and other toys from interrupting the flow of conversation on the patio. In addition to separate play space, these outdoor living areas are perfect for a meditation or yoga nook, or a relaxed fire pit area. Or, splurge on a sport court for your family. Not only healthy and promoting an active lifestyle, they can "fill up" a large yard with functional outdoor play space that's done in a professional and attractive way. On the next couple of pages are more ideas for a backyard sport court. Playing outside is once again for the young, and the young at heart.

Whether dividing the outdoors into "rooms" or sharing the space for activities, it is important to be aware of how the outdoor living space will be used. Specialty landscaping and outdoor storage can be used to keep various activities from interrupting one another. However you choose to use the space, remember to take advantage of every corner for a retreat ideal for you, not so far from home.

LIVELY OR LAZY?
Do you prefer active areas
or relaxed areas
for your outdoor space?

building a backyard
SPORT COURT

When the weather is warm, it is a great time for you and your kids to spend time playing outdoors away from the sedentary indoor activities. One of the best investments you can make for your family is a game court in your backyard. The kids will not only be safer in the comfort of your backyard, but you will know what they are doing. It also gets them off the couch and away from electronic devices, while also promoting a healthy and active lifestyle. Whether you like shooting some hoops, tossing the baseball around, or smacking a tennis ball, the choice is yours with either a single sport, or multi-sport game court.

so, where to start?

Think about what sports you want the court to encompass. Does your family have a favorite sport? Is this just going to be a place for the kids to shoot the basketball around, or do you want a court large enough for the entire family to play? Once you've decided what sports you want to be able to play, it will be easier to gauge the size court you will need. If adding additional activity into your daily life is something you crave as well, then by all means think of the adults in the family too and include a sport court that promotes a healthier lifestyle for all family members.

do I have enough room?

Space can be a limiting factor when deciding what court you want. So, measure the space you have to work in your backyard. If you want a court with a 3 point line you will need at least a 25' x 45' area. For net sports such as volleyball or tennis, a 30' x 60' area allows for full court volleyball. This gives you a general guideline of the size space you will need.

When you've established how much space you have, check with the building department in your specific area to make sure they don't have any regulations you must follow or they don't require you to have a permit to build your dream court.

Nothing should be stopping you now from building your very own game court! Building a court is a big construction project to handle on your own, but can also be done if you're on a small budget. You can always build in stages starting with a concrete platform and a basketball hoop and enjoy that for a year, and then next year add a sports tile surface and landscaping.

phase 1 of building:

If your property is relatively flat, this first phase of building will not be much work, but if not, then more work will be required. First, start by stripping the sod away. Next, the area where your court will sit will have to be leveled if it's not already. Use a plate compactor that can be rented from a local hardware store if you are taking on the construction yourself. Courts can collect water especially if you live in an area that gets a lot of rain. Consider investing in a drainage system to eliminate water damage your court could incur.

phase 2 of building:

It's time to choose the base of your court. Generally the base is built with concrete because it will not require maintenance every year. There are other options such as asphalt, compacted bases, or modular bases. A compacted base is created by layering smaller and smaller stone and then compacting those stones. This type of base is not as permanent as concrete would be. The choice is yours, though.

If you've chosen concrete as the base you could just paint the surface and call it a sports court. However, more injuries are likely to occur this way, and if you have the budget to go ahead and make the court look nice and feel like it has a bit of a cushion, then why not do it?

The most effective cushioned surface to put over the concrete would be a modular surface designed to absorb the shock your legs would normally receive, and this type of surface allows water to pass through and flow off the court. Most modular surfaces are also easy to assemble coming in pieces that snap together. They also come in fun colors that will add style to your sport court.

the final phase:

This is the fun phase of building when you get to add all the finishing touches to your court. So, put up the nets and the hoops and start playing. If you went with a full volleyball court, you could put a basketball hoop along the side of the court and use the hoop to hold up one side of the volleyball net. Get creative and make the most out of your sport court!

Depending on the climate in the area where you live, an outdoor sport court might not be conducive to your area. Consider moving the activities inside to an indoor sport court if that is the case.

Page 72 and 73, all photos courtesy of Sport Court St. Louis, sportcourtstlouis.com; Page 73, top: Plan #101D-0066, copyright by designer/architect, plan available for purchase at houseplansandmore.com.

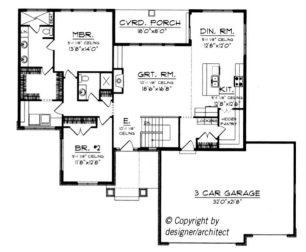

PLAN #909-051D-0800

Dimensions:	66'8" W x 55' D
Heated Sq. Ft.:	1,709
Bedrooms: 2	Bathrooms: 2
Exterior Walls:	2" x 6"

Foundation: Basement standard; crawl space or slab for an additional fee

See index on page 104 for more information

PLAN #909-011D-0664

Dimensions:	64' W x 67'6" D
Heated Sq. Ft.:	2,576
Bonus Sq. Ft.:	374
Bedrooms: 3	Bathrooms: 2½
Exterior Walls:	2" x 6"

Foundation: Joisted continuous footings standard; basement for an additional fee

See index on page 104 for more information

Optional Second Floor 374 sq. ft.

First Floor 2,576 sq. ft.

PLAN #909-011D-0280

Dimensions: 70' W x 50' D
Heated Sq. Ft.: 1,868
Bedrooms: 3 Bathrooms: 2
Exterior Walls: 2" x 6"
Foundation: Joisted crawl space or
post & beam standard; slab or
basement for an additional fee
See index on page 104 for more information

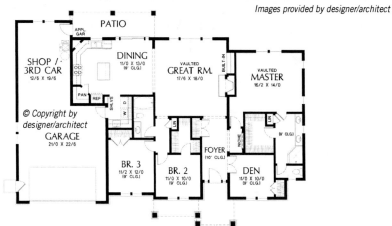

© Copyright by
designer/architect

PLAN #909-013D-0230

Dimensions: 53'8" W x 60'1" D
Heated Sq. Ft.: 1,800
Bonus Sq. Ft.: 3,124
Bedrooms: 3 Bathrooms: 2½
Foundation: Walk-out basement
standard; crawl space or slab for an
additional fee
See index on page 104 for more information

© Copyright by
designer/architect

Optional Lower Level
1,900 sq. ft.

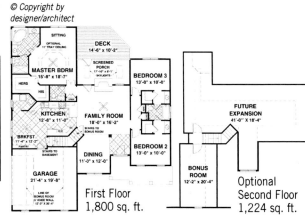

First Floor
1,800 sq. ft.

Optional
Second Floor
1,224 sq. ft.

PLAN #909-101D-0077

Dimensions:	68' W x 77' D
Heated Sq. Ft.:	2,422
Bonus Sq. Ft.:	1,491
Bedrooms: 2	Bathrooms: 2½
Exterior Walls:	2" x 6"

Foundation: Basement or daylight basement, please specify when ordering

See index on page 104 for more information

Images provided by designer/architect

FEATURES

- Rustic ranch living has been achieved in this beautiful home
- The kitchen enjoys a massive island that overlooks the great room and dining area
- The master bedroom is tucked away nicely and includes a huge walk-in shower, and an oversized walk-in closet in its private bath
- The spacious mud room/laundry will keep everyone organized
- The optional lower level has an additional 1,491 square feet of living area and includes two additional bedrooms, a full bath, a family room with wet bar, and an exercise room
- 2-car side entry garage and 1-car front entry garage

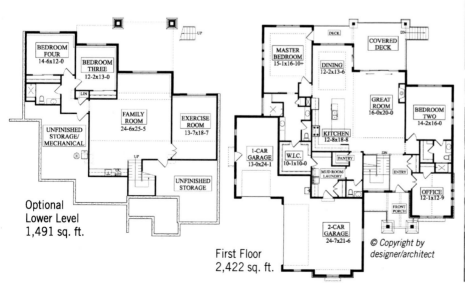

Optional
Lower Level
1,491 sq. ft.

First Floor
2,422 sq. ft.

© Copyright by
designer/architect

CALL 1-800-373-2646   ONLINE houseplansandmore.com

PLAN #909-024D-0813

Dimensions: 36' W x 68'" D
Heated Sq. Ft.: 1,728
Bedrooms: 3   Bathrooms: 3
Foundation: Pilings
See index on page 104 for more information

Images provided by designer/architect

FEATURES

- This raised one-story home is ideal for coastal regions and offers parking underneath the home
- The kitchen overlooks both the dining and living areas
- The private master bedroom has deck access, a walk-in closet, and a private bath with a free-standing tub as well as a walk-in shower
- An oversized elevator makes reaching the main floor easy from the parking area underneath

© Copyright by designer/architect

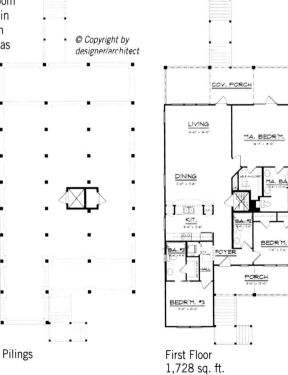

Pilings

First Floor
1,728 sq. ft.

CALL 1-800-373-2646   ONLINE houseplansandmore.com   77

Images provided by designer/architect

PLAN #909-028D-0100

Dimensions: 46' W x 42'6" D
Heated Sq. Ft.: 1,311
Bedrooms: 3   Bathrooms: 2
Exterior Walls: 2" x 6"
Foundation: Crawl space or slab,
please specify when ordering
See index on page 104 for more information

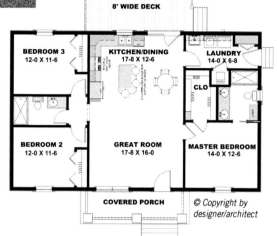

© Copyright by designer/architect

Images provided by designer/architect

PLAN #909-091D-0524

Dimensions: 69' W x 59'6" D
Heated Sq. Ft.: 2,480
Bonus Sq. Ft.: 361
Bedrooms: 4   Bathrooms: 3½
Exterior Walls: 2" x 6"
Foundation: Basement standard;
crawl space or slab for an additional fee
See index on page 104 for more information

Optional Second Floor
361 sq. ft.

First Floor
2,480 sq. ft.

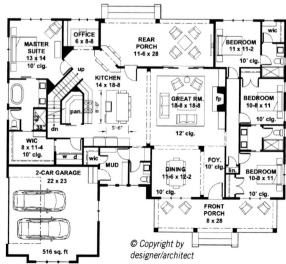

© Copyright by designer/architect

CALL 1-800-373-2646   **ONLINE** houseplansandmore.com

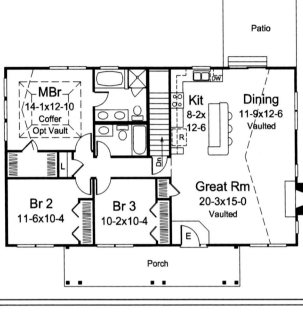

Garage
23-4x23-4

© Copyright by
designer/architect

PLAN #909-121D-0025

Images provided by designer/architect

Dimensions: 50' W x 34'6" D
Heated Sq. Ft.: 1,368
Bedrooms: 3   Bathrooms: 2
Foundation: Basement standard;
crawl space or slab for an additional
fee

See index on page 104 for more information

Patio

MBr
14-1x12-10
Coffer
Opt Vault

Kit
8-2x
12-6

Dining
11-9x12-6
Vaulted

Dn

Br 2
11-6x10-4

Br 3
10-2x10-4

Great Rm
20-3x15-0
Vaulted

E

Porch

PLAN #909-121D-0035

Images provided by designer/architect

Dimensions: 45'8" W x 72'4" D
Heated Sq. Ft.: 1,759
Bedrooms: 3   Bathrooms: 2
Foundation: Basement standard;
crawl space or slab for an additional
fee

See index on page 104 for more information

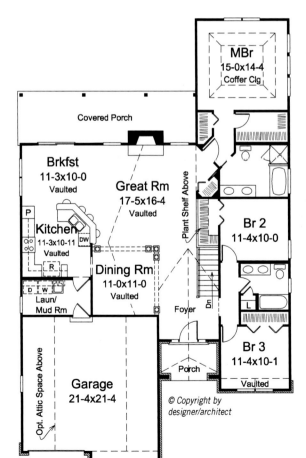

Covered Porch

MBr
15-0x14-4
Coffer Clg

Brkfst
11-3x10-0
Vaulted

Great Rm
17-5x16-4
Vaulted

Plant Shelf Above

Kitchen
11-3x10-11
Vaulted

Br 2
11-4x10-0

Dining Rm
11-0x11-0
Vaulted

Foyer

Dn

**Laun/
Mud Rm**

D W

Opt. Attic Space Above

Garage
21-4x21-4

Porch

Br 3
11-4x10-1
Vaulted

© Copyright by
designer/architect

PLAN #909-011D-0649

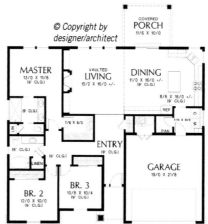

© Copyright by
designer/architect

Dimensions:	49' W x 53' D
Heated Sq. Ft.:	1,605
Bedrooms: 3	Bathrooms: 2
Exterior Walls:	2" x 6"

Foundation: Joisted continuous
footings standard; basement for an
additional fee

See index on page 104 for more information

PLAN #909-128D-0309

Dimensions:	41'7" W x 56'6" D
Heated Sq. Ft.:	1,504
Bedrooms: 3	Bathrooms: 2

Foundation: Crawl space or
basement, please specify when
ordering

See index on page 104 for more information

© Copyright by
designer/architect

CALL 1-800-373-2646   ONLINE houseplansandmore.com

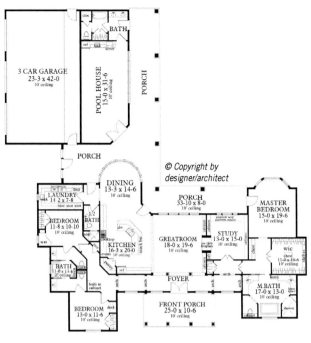

PLAN #909-084D-0075

Dimensions:	96'8" W x 100' D
Heated Sq. Ft.:	3,613
Bedrooms: 3	Bathrooms: 4
Exterior Walls:	2" x 6"

Foundation: Slab standard; basement
or crawl space for an additional fee
See index on page 104 for more information

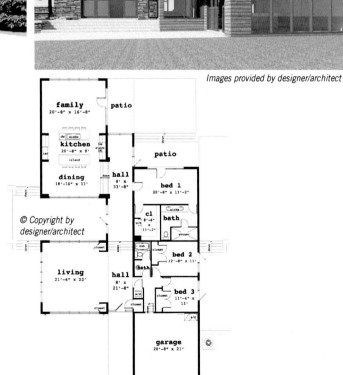

PLAN #909-152D-0084

Dimensions:	52' W x 96' D
Heated Sq. Ft.:	2,806
Bedrooms: 3	Bathrooms: 2
Exterior Walls:	2" x 6"
Foundation:	Slab

See index on page 104 for more information

PLAN #909-051D-1007

Dimensions: 108'8" W x 46'8" D
Heated Sq. Ft.: 4,246
Bedrooms: 4   Bathrooms: 4
Exterior Walls: 2" x 6"
Foundation: Walk-out basement
standard; crawl space or slab for an
additional fee

See index on page 104 for more information

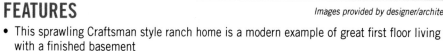

Images provided by designer/architect

FEATURES

- This sprawling Craftsman style ranch home is a modern example of great first floor living with a finished basement
- The kitchen, great room and nook blend together to create an open concept living space that boasts a fireplace with built-in cabinets on both sides
- The first floor master suite includes double walk-in closets, a private bath with a spa style tub, a tray ceiling and an additional sitting area
- Three bedrooms, each with their own walk-in closet, two full baths, and a large family room are found in the lower level with doors that lead to a patio
- 3-car front entry garage

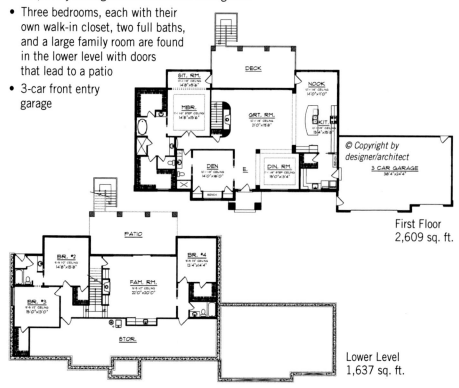

© Copyright by designer/architect

First Floor
2,609 sq. ft.

Lower Level
1,637 sq. ft.

CALL 1-800-373-2646   **ONLINE** houseplansandmore.com

PLAN #909-161D-0013

Dimensions:	99'4" W x 87'10" D
Heated Sq. Ft.:	3,264
Bedrooms: 3	Bathrooms: 3½
Exterior Walls:	2" x 6"
Foundation:	Crawl space

See index on page 104 for more information

Images provided by designer/architect

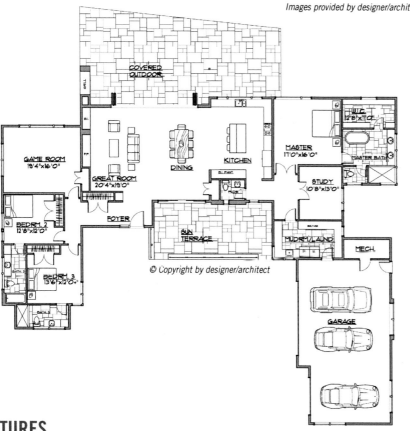

© Copyright by designer/architect

FEATURES

- This stunning modern home offers the open floor plan and high ceilings homeowners want today
- The split bedroom floor plan has the master suite tucked behind the kitchen and near a quiet study
- There are lovely outdoor spaces in the front as well as the back of the home
- The great room enjoys a sleek fireplace that can also be seen by the kitchen and dining space
- 3-car side entry garage

Alternate
Slab or
Crawl Space
Layout

Images provided by designer/architect

PLAN #909-001D-0024

Dimensions: 68' W x 38' D
Heated Sq. Ft.:   1,360
Bedrooms: 3   Bathrooms: 2
Foundation: Basement standard;
crawl space or slab for an additional
fee

See index on page 104 for more information

© Copyright by
designer/architect

Patio

Garage
22'-4"x23'-5"

Kit/Dining
17'-6"x14'-6"

MBr
12'-9"x14'-6"

Work Shop
10'-8"x6'-0"

Family
17'-6"x14'-7"

Br 3
12'-1"x11'-3"

Br 2
12'-2"x11'-3"

Covered Porch
23'-0"x8'-0"

Images provided by designer/architect

PLAN #909-051D-0757

Dimensions: 55' W x 51'8" D
Heated Sq. Ft.:   1,501
Bedrooms: 3   Bathrooms: 2
Exterior Walls: 2" x 6"
Foundation: Basement standard;
crawl space or slab for an additional
fee

See index on page 104 for more information

CVRD. PORCH
16'0"x10'4"

GRT. RM.
VAULTED CEILING
17'8"x14'6"

MBR.
10'-1 1/8" STEP CEILING
14'0"x12'0"

BR. #3
9'-1 1/8" CEILING
10'0"x11'0"

DIN.
VAULTED CEILING
14'0"x11'6"

KIT.
VAULTED CEILING
10'6"x12'4"

BR. #2
9'-1 1/8" CEILING
11'0"x11'0"

E.
VAULTED
CEILING

3 CAR GARAGE
29'4"x21'8"

© Copyright by
designer/architect

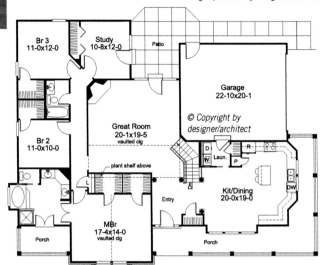

PLAN #909-007D-0055

Dimensions: 67' W x 51'4" D
Heated Sq. Ft.: 2,029
Bedrooms: 3   Bathrooms: 2
Foundation: Basement standard;
crawl space or slab for an additional fee

See index on page 104 for more information

Br 3
11-0x12-0

Study
10-8x12-0

Patio

Garage
22-10x20-1

Great Room
20-1x19-5
vaulted clg

© Copyright by
designer/architect

Br 2
11-0x10-0

plant shelf above

Laun.

Kit/Dining
20-0x19-0

Entry

MBr
17-4x14-0
vaulted clg

Porch

Porch

PLAN #909-077D-0043

Dimensions: 64' W x 45'10" D
Heated Sq. Ft.: 1,751
Bedrooms: 3   Bathrooms: 2
Foundation: Slab, basement or crawl space, please specify when ordering

See index on page 104 for more information

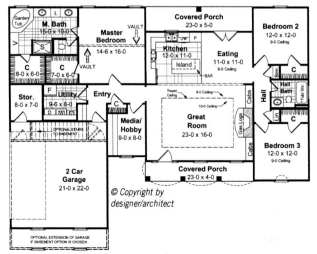

Garden Tub

M. Bath
15-0 x 10-0

Master
Bedroom
14-6 x 16-0

VAULT

Covered Porch
23-0 x 5-0

Kitchen
12-0 x 11-0

Island

Eating
11-0 x 11-0
9-0 Ceiling

Bedroom 2
12-0 x 12-0
9-0 Ceiling

C 8-0 x 6-0   C 7-0 x 6-0
VAULT

Stor.
8-0 x 7-0

Utility
9-6 x 8-0

Entry

Media/
Hobby
9-0 x 8-0

Great
Room
23-0 x 16-0

Hall
Bath

Bedroom 3
12-0 x 12-0
9-0 Ceiling

2 Car
Garage
21-0 x 22-0

OPTIONAL STAIRS
TO BASEMENT

Covered Porch
23-0 x 4-0

© Copyright by
designer/architect

OPTIONAL EXTENSION OF GARAGE
IF BASEMENT OPTION IS CHOSEN.

PLAN #909-051D-0974

Dimensions: 60' W x 73' D
Heated Sq. Ft.: 1,736
Bedrooms: 2   Bathrooms: 2
Exterior Walls: 2" x 6"
Foundation: Basement standard;
crawl space or slab for an additional
fee
See index on page 104 for more information

Images provided by designer/architect

FEATURES

- A deep Craftsman style porch greets all those who enter this home and has enough space for a swing or rocking chairs
- The ever-popular open floor plan reigns in this home featuring sunny dining and great rooms with a kitchen overlooking it all
- The kitchen has a unique and functional hidden pantry that seamlessly blends with the rest of the cabinets
- The super-private master bedroom enjoys a spacious walk-in closet extending from the bath
- 3-car front entry garage

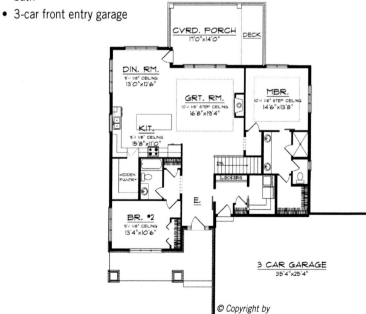

CALL 1-800-373-2646   **ONLINE** houseplansandmore.com

PLAN #909-101D-0089

Dimensions:	70' W x 77'9" D
Heated Sq. Ft.:	2,509
Bonus Sq. Ft.:	1,645
Bedrooms: 4	Bathrooms: 2½
Exterior Walls:	2" x 6"
Foundation:	Basement

See index on page 104 for more information

FEATURES

- The wrap-around porch welcomes you into this beautiful home designed with a popular Modern Farmhouse flair
- The split bedroom layout is perfect for families
- The dining, kitchen and great room are open, creating a large area, perfect for all activities
- With a walk-in closet, dual sinks and a generously sized bedroom, the master suite makes the perfect place to retire for the evening
- The optional lower level has an additional 1,645 square feet of living area and has two bedrooms, a bath, and a rec room with a wet bar
- 3-car side entry garage

Images provided by designer/architect

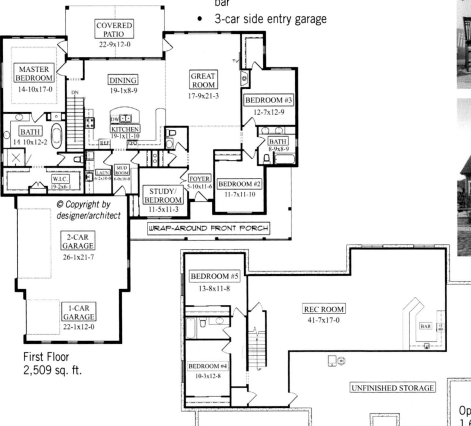

First Floor
2,509 sq. ft.

Optional Lower Level
1,645 sq. ft.

7 OUTDOOR TRENDS
you need in your life now

1 **FRONT PORCHES ARE IN FASHION** Today's popular floor plans are including plentiful front porches that have enough space to create an outdoor living space. Helping to create a sense of community in a neighborhood, these porches offer an opportunity to enjoy the outdoors and have face-to-face contact with people in their neighborhood. With many homes now featuring oversized living spaces in the front of the home, outdoor living has extended not just to the backyard, but to the front, too. Providing curb appeal and a welcoming feel to the front exterior, these covered porches are now offering cozy seating, soft lighting, and maybe even a water element for a tranquil feel. If a home doesn't have a front porch, then often a courtyard is created providing a front patio space that welcomes people in. Other fun focal points include a statement front door. Whether it's a door with a unique window, a trendy Dutch-Style door, or a door painted in a bold unexpected color, a statement door might as well say, "Come on in!"

Page 88, top to bottom, left: Traditional Spring Collection, target.com; Boho front porch chic, camillestyles.com; middle: Karen Kempf Interiors (karen-kempf.com) featured in *Milwaukee Magazine* ©2012, Adam Ryan Morris, staff photographer; middle, right: Inviting front porch swing, modern-glam.com; bottom: Stylish farmhouse front porch, seekinglavenderlane.com. Page 89, top, right: Minimalist patio, emerahome.com; Black and white patio, zdesignathome.com; Bottom: Minimalist chic from article by Melissa Dalton in *Dwell Magazine*, Haris Kenjar, photographer.

2 IT'S ALL BLACK & WHITE

It's no secret with the popularity of modern farmhouse style homes, that black and white color schemes are the top choice in interior design right now. Well, that color palette has extended itself to the outdoors, too. Using a similar color palette to your interior spaces not only looks attractive, but it creates a visual extension that is seamless inside and out. Plus, classic black and white palettes are timeless, classy, clean and tend to look great with many types of architecture whether your home is industrial modern or a modern farmhouse. If you just can't stick with black and white and need a little color in your life, then go bold with citrus brights in orange, yellow, and lime, or choose these hot trendy colors - bright coral, pink, or emerald green.

3 MINIMALIST, CLEAN SPACES

Think Scandinavian style chic! Part Utilitarian and part Ikea®-inspired, homeowners are craving good function and clean un-cluttered dwellings. Perfect for escaping the clutter of work, and the outside world, these types of spaces are calming and tranquil and it should come as no surprise that our outdoor spaces are quickly turning to this minimalist style of living with sleeker furniture styles that have far less ornamentation than we've seen previously. Solid plastic pieces or sleek metal styles all have a place on today's patio, too.

4 MIXED MATERIALS AREN'T A MIXED MESSAGE

Say goodbye to matching your patio furniture and look for several types of materials to create your outdoor space. Wooden benches sit alongside metal end tables and a rope swing may be a fun add-in. Mix glass accessories, metal, wrought iron, and wood and create a casual space with thoughtful choices. To soften up all of those hard surfaces look to oversized pillows you can throw down on the patio floor, outdoor rugs, or take a cozy throw blanket outside when the weather becomes chilly.

5 THE KITCHEN IS CLOSED, BUT THE BAR IS OPEN

Outdoor kitchens still remain popular, and so do any fire elements such as a cozy fireplace or fire pit, but if you're adding a social spot outdoors, think more happy hour and less dinnertime. Outdoor bar spaces are quickly becoming a popular, fun choice that are playful and much more affordable than adding an outdoor kitchen. Find a neat rolling cart and recycle into an outdoor bar for something inexpensive and portable, or invest in a built-in area with a refrigerator and high-top tables. The ideas are endless and this addition to your outdoor space may have you saying, "last call" much more frequently.

Page 90, top to bottom, left: Huron Lounge Collection, westelm. com; Acacia Expanding Bar Table, SKU#65743225, bedbathand- beyond.com; Fafavieh Monterey Bar Table, bedbathandbeyond. com; top, right: Patio with mixed materials, greenvillejournal.com, Katarzyna Bialasiewicz Photographee.eu, photographer; bottom, right: On-point outdoor bar space with garage door above, trendir. com; Page 91, top, left to right: Garden living wall, theartinlife.com; Living wall becomes art, sagegreenlife.com; bottom: Loa Outdoor Furniture as seen on behance.net.

6 ECO-FRIENDLY EXTERIORS

Homeowners are reducing their carbon footprint by creating living walls composed of plants, and herbs that can be utilized easily in an indoor or outdoor kitchen. Add some LED lighting that relies on the sun for its power and you've created a eco-fun and friendly outdoor oasis. If you choose to add a deck, then look to sustainable choices or composite decking. Many stylish rugs, and furniture are made from recycled products giving these things a new useful life on your very own sustain able and responsible patio.

7 BRIGHT LIGHTING

Continuing with the theme of carrying the indoors outside, lighting is an important element in making your outdoor space shine. From candles made with essential oils to LED illuminated umbrellas, or even nostalgic tiki torches, there are countless choices for lighting your backyard space and creating that inviting ambiance that draws people in to relax and stay awhile. The ever-popular fire pits and fireplaces are also great illumination choices especially in the cooler months.

Whether you choose a couple of these trends, or find a way to implement all of them, your outdoor living area will become a place that rivals, or even surpasses your favorite indoor space. Creating a space that uses subtle colors, modern lines and an abundance of texture will keep your outdoor space interesting and relevant.

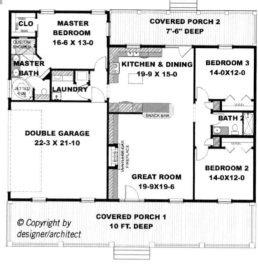

PLAN #909-028D-0112

Dimensions: 56'" W x 52' D
Heated Sq. Ft.:   1,611
Bedrooms: 3   Bathrooms: 2
Exterior Walls: 2" x 6"
Foundation: Crawl space or slab,
please specify when ordering

See index on page 104 for more information

CLO

MASTER
BEDROOM
16-6 X 13-0

COVERED PORCH 2
7'-6" DEEP

MASTER
BATH

KITCHEN & DINING
19-9 X 15-0

BEDROOM 3
14-0X12-0

JETTED
TUB

LAUNDRY

SNACK BAR

BATH 2

DOUBLE GARAGE
22-3 X 21-10

VENEER-GAS
FIREPLACE

GREAT ROOM
19-9X19-6

BEDROOM 2
14-0X12-0

© Copyright by
designer/architect

COVERED PORCH 1
10 FT. DEEP

PLAN #909-166D-0003

Dimensions: 56'6" W x 77'5" D
Heated Sq. Ft.:   2,359
Bedrooms: 3   Bathrooms: 2
Exterior Walls: 2" x 6"
Foundation: Slab

See index on page 104 for more information

MASTER BDRM
13'-8" X 17'-0"

MASTER BATH
10'-9" X 12'-11"

COVERED PATIO
23'-2" X 8'-6"

LAUNDRY
7'-10" X 7'-0"

MSTR CLOSET
13'-11" X 7'-4"

LIVING
20'-10" X 17'-6"

KITCHEN
14'-6" X 14'-1"

NOOK
9'-8" X 11'-6"

COVERED PATIO
9'-4" X 19'-0"

DINING
14'-8" X 10'-6"

BUTLER
5'-4" X 5'-10"

VANITY
6'-1" X 5'-6"

PAN
4'-3" X 6'-0"

FAM ENTRY
9'-1" X 6'-1"

ENTRY
6'-2" X 16'-5"

BATH
5'-1" X 4'-10"

GARAGE
21'-0" X 21'-6"

COVERED PORCH
8'-9" X 9'-2"

BEDROOM 2
12'-0" X 11'-0"

BEDROOM 3
12'-0" X 14'-4"

COURTYARD
14'-8" X 8'-2"

© Copyright by
designer/architect

PLAN #909-155D-0170

Dimensions: 60'6" W x 64'8" D
Heated Sq. Ft.: 1,897
Bedrooms: 4   Bathrooms: 2
Foundation: Crawl space or slab standard; basement or daylight basement for an additional fee

See index on page 104 for more information

Images provided by designer/architect

PLAN #909-155D-0120

Dimensions: 78'7" W x 90'4" D
Heated Sq. Ft.: 3,004
Bedrooms: 3   Bathrooms: 3½
Exterior Walls: 2" x 6"
Foundation: Crawl space or slab standard; daylight basement or basement for an additional fee

See index on page 104 for more information

Images provided by designer/architect

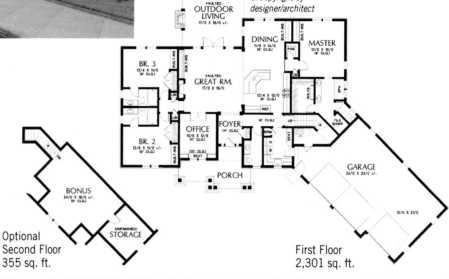

© Copyright by
designer/architect

PLAN #909-011D-0606

Dimensions: 94'10" W x 76'11" D
Heated Sq. Ft.:   2,301
Bonus Sq. Ft.:   355
Bedrooms: 3   Bathrooms: 3½
Exterior Walls: 2" x 6"
Foundation: Joisted crawl space or
post & beam standard; basement for
an additional fee

See index on page 104 for more information

Optional
Second Floor
355 sq. ft.

First Floor
2,301 sq. ft.

PLAN #909-167D-0001

Dimensions: 59'6" W x 60' D
Heated Sq. Ft.:   2,017
Bedrooms: 3   Bathrooms: 3
Exterior Walls: 2" x 6"
Foundation: Crawl space standard;
slab for an additional fee

See index on page 104 for more information

© Copyright by
designer/architect

CALL 1-800-373-2646   **ONLINE** houseplansandmore.com

PLAN #909-013D-0235

Dimensions: 71'2" W x 64'6" D
Heated Sq. Ft.: 2,140
Bonus Sq. Ft.: 1,535
Bedrooms: 3   Bathrooms: 3
Foundation: Crawl space standard; basement or slab for an additional fee

See index on page 104 for more information

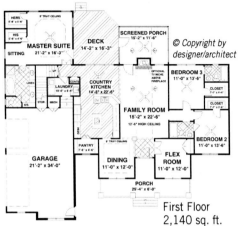

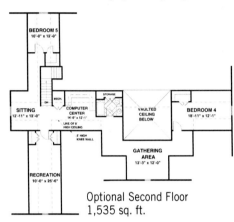

First Floor
2,140 sq. ft.

Optional Second Floor
1,535 sq. ft.

Optional
Second Floor
359 sq. ft.

PLAN #909-077D-0128

Dimensions: 69' W x 59'10" D
Heated Sq. Ft.: 2,000
Bonus Sq. Ft.: 359
Bedrooms: 3   Bathrooms: 2½
Foundation: Slab or crawl space standard; for basement version, please see Plan #077D-0131 at houseplansandmore.com

See index on page 104 for more information

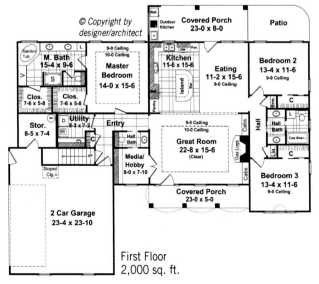

First Floor
2,000 sq. ft.

PLAN #909-011D-0637

Dimensions: 46'6" W x 54' D
Heated Sq. Ft.:   1,744
Bedrooms: 3   Bathrooms: 2½
Exterior Walls: 2" x 6"
Foundation: Engineered joists with crawl space standard; slab or basement for an additional fee
See index on page 104 for more information

© Copyright by designer/architect

PLAN #909-091D-0511

Dimensions: 78'11" W x 65'5" D
Heated Sq. Ft.:   2,150
Bonus Sq. Ft.:   733
Bedrooms: 4   Bathrooms: 3
Exterior Walls: 2" x 6"
Foundation: Basement or crawl space standard; daylight basement, slab or walk-out basement for an additional fee
See index on page 104 for more information

Optional Second Floor 733 sq. ft.

© Copyright by designer/architect

First Floor 2,150 sq. ft.

CALL 1-800-373-2646   ONLINE houseplansandmore.com

PLAN #909-011D-0655

Dimensions:	60' W x 62' D
Heated Sq. Ft.:	2,707
Bonus Sq. Ft.:	375

Bedrooms: 4   Bathrooms: 2½

Exterior Walls:	2" x 6"
Foundation:	Slab

See index on page 104 for more information

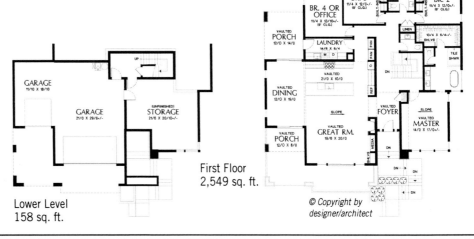

Lower Level
158 sq. ft.

First Floor
2,549 sq. ft.

© Copyright by
designer/architect

PLAN #909-141D-0246

Dimensions: 54'7" W x 38' D
Heated Sq. Ft.:   1,234
Bedrooms: 2   Bathrooms: 2
Foundation: Slab or crawl space,
please specify when ordering
See index on page 104 for more information

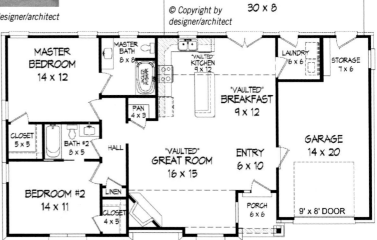

© Copyright by
designer/architect

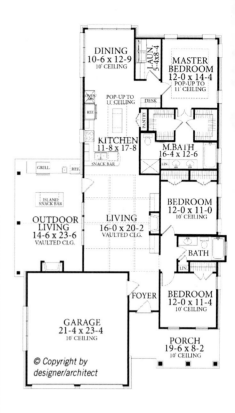

PLAN #909-084D-0086

Dimensions: 45'4" W x 76' D
Heated Sq. Ft.: 1,725
Bedrooms: 3   Bathrooms: 2
Foundation: Slab standard; crawl
space for an additional fee
See index on page 104 for more information

Images provided by designer/architect

Floor plan labels:
- DINING 10-6 x 12-9, 10' CEILING
- LAUN. 5-4x8-4
- MASTER BEDROOM 12-0 x 14-4, POP-UP TO 11' CEILING
- POP-UP TO LR CEILING
- DESK
- PANTRY
- KITCHEN 11-8 x 17-8
- M.BATH 16-4 x 12-6
- SNACK BAR
- GRILL / REF.
- ISLAND SNACK BAR
- BEDROOM 12-0 x 11-0, 10' CEILING
- OUTDOOR LIVING 14-6 x 23-6, VAULTED CLG.
- LIVING 16-0 x 20-2, VAULTED CLG.
- BATH
- FOYER
- GARAGE 21-4 x 23-4, 10' CEILING
- BEDROOM 12-0 x 11-4, 10' CEILING
- PORCH 19-6 x 8-2, 10' CEILING
- © Copyright by designer/architect

Images provided by designer/architect

PLAN #909-091D-0516

Dimensions: 71' W x 73'2" D
Heated Sq. Ft.: 2,287
Bonus Sq. Ft.: 535
Bedrooms: 3   Bathrooms: 2½
Exterior Walls: 2" x 6"
Foundation: Basement or crawl space
standard; slab for an additional fee
See index on page 104 for more information

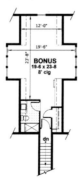

Optional
Second Floor
535 sq. ft.

BONUS 19-6 x 23-8, 8' clg

First Floor
2,287 sq. ft.

Floor plan labels:
- GARAGE 23 x 26, 10'-6" clg
- opt. rear gar. door for gar. seating
- PATIO
- POOL NOT INCLUDED
- MUD 9' clg / lockers
- RESOURCE 9-7 x 10, 9' clg
- REAR PORCH 9-6 x 29
- BEDROOM 10-6 x 11, 9' clg
- KITCHEN 13-8 x 19, 9' clg
- GREAT ROOM 16-8 x 17, 12' clg
- MASTER SUITE 13 x 16, vaulted clg
- BEDROOM 11 x 11, 9' clg
- DINING 11 x 16-8
- WIC 7 x 13
- PORCH 7 x 23-6
- © Copyright by designer/architect

First Floor
1,269 sq. ft.

© Copyright by
designer/architect

Optional
Lower Level
1,269 sq. ft.

Images provided by designer/architect

PLAN #909-032D-1073

Dimensions:	38' W x 38' D
Heated Sq. Ft.:	1,269
Bonus Sq. Ft.:	1,269
Bedrooms: 2	Bathrooms: 1
Exterior Walls:	2" x 6"

Foundation: Walk-out basement
standard; crawl space, floating slab
or monolithic slab for an additional
fee
See index on page 104 for more information

Images provided by designer/architect

PLAN #909-032D-1135

Dimensions:	65' W x 50'" D
Heated Sq. Ft.:	1,788
Bonus Sq. Ft.:	1,788
Bedrooms: 2	Bathrooms: 2

Foundation: Basement standard;
crawl space, floating slab or
monolithic slab for an additional fee
See index on page 104 for more information

Optional
Lower Level
1,788 sq. ft.

First Floor
1,788 sq. ft.

© Copyright by
designer/architect

PLAN #909-011D-0229

Dimensions:	60' W x 111' D
Heated Sq. Ft.:	2,904
Bedrooms: 3	Bathrooms: 3½
Exterior Walls:	2" x 6"

Foundation: Joisted crawl space, post & beam, or TrusJoist floor system standard; slab or basement for an additional fee

See index on page 104 for more information

FEATURES

- This stunning one-story has all of the essentials for great family living
- The kitchen features an island facing out over the dining area with a nearby sitting and great room
- The bedrooms are all in close proximity to one another for convenience
- A cozy vaulted den has a fireplace and a bay window
- The outdoor living space has a fireplace and built-in grill
- 3-car side entry garage

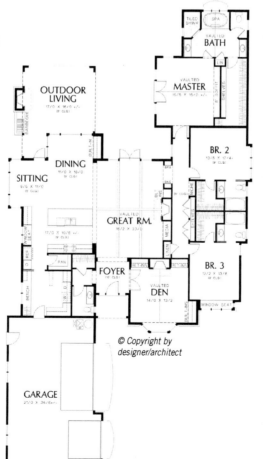

© Copyright by designer/architect

PLAN #909-056D-0104

Dimensions: 63'1" W x 41'10" D
Heated Sq. Ft.: 1,925
Bedrooms: 3   Bathrooms: 2½
Foundation: Slab

See index on page 104 for more information

© Copyright by designer/architect

PLAN #909-155D-0065

Dimensions: 72'6" W x 64'8" D
Heated Sq. Ft.: 1,897
Bonus Sq. Ft.: 373
Bedrooms: 4   Bathrooms: 2
Exterior Walls: 2" x 6"
Foundation: Crawl space or slab standard; basement or daylight basement for an additional fee

See index on page 104 for more information

Optional Second Floor 373 sq. ft.

© Copyright by designer/architect

First Floor 1,897 sq. ft.

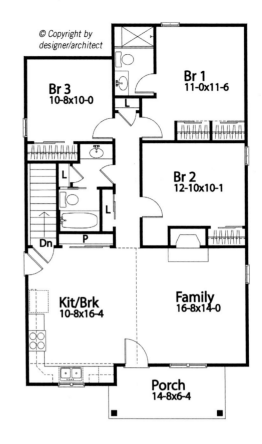

Images provided by designer/architect

PLAN #909-058D-0223

Dimensions: 28' W x 48' D
Heated Sq. Ft.: 1,149
Bedrooms: 3   Bathrooms: 2
Foundation: Basement

See index on page 104 for more information

Br 3
10-8x10-0

Br 1
11-0x11-6

Br 2
12-10x10-1

Dn

P

Kit/Brk
10-8x16-4

Family
16-8x14-0

Porch
14-8x6-4

Images provided by designer/architect

PLAN #909-155D-0055

Dimensions: 51' W x 56'6" D
Heated Sq. Ft.: 1,745
Bedrooms: 3   Bathrooms: 2
Foundation: Crawl space or slab standard; daylight basement or basement for an additional fee

See index on page 104 for more information

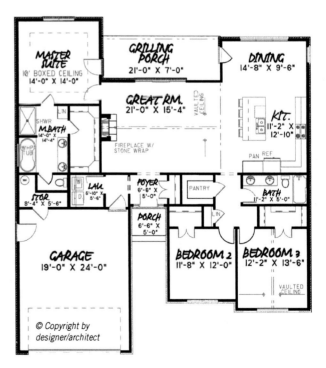

MASTER SUITE
10' BOXED CEILING
14'-0" X 14'-0"

GRILLING PORCH
21'-0" X 7'-0"

DINING
14'-8" X 9'-6"

GREAT RM.
21'-0" X 15'-4"
VAULTED CEILING

KIT.
11'-2" X 12'-10"

MBATH
14'-0" X 14'-4"

SHWR

WHP TUB

FIREPLACE W/ STONE WRAP

PAN REF.

STOR
8'-4" X 5'-6"

LAU.
5'-10" X 5'-6"

FOYER
6'-6" X 5'-0"

PANTRY

BATH
11'-2" X 5'-0"

PORCH
6'-6" X 5'-0"

GARAGE
19'-0" X 24'-0"

BEDROOM 2
11'-8" X 12'-0"

BEDROOM 3
12'-2" X 13'-6"
VAULTED CEILING

HOME PLAN INDEX

PLEASE NOTE: Plan pricing is subject to change without notice. For current pricing, visit houseplansandmore.com, or call us at 1-800-373-2646.

Plan Number	Square Feet	PDF File	5-Sets	CAD File	Material List	Page
909-001D-0024	1,360	$889	$889	$1,389	$125	84
909-001D-0031	1,501	$989	$989	$1,589	$125	47
909-005D-0001	1,400	$889	$889	$1,389	$125	30
909-007D-0055	2,029	$1,089	$1,089	$1,789	$125	85
909-007D-0060	1,268	$889	$889	$1,389	$125	18
909-007D-0113	2,547	$1,189	$1,189	$1,989	$125	54
909-007D-0124	1,944	$989	$989	$1,589	$125	35
909-007D-0136	1,532	$989	$989	$1,589	$125	62
909-007D-0140	1,591	$989	$989	$1,589	$125	66
909-007D-0146	1,929	$989	$989	$1,589	$125	59
909-007D-0162	1,519	$989	$989	$1,589	$125	38
909-007D-5060	1,344	$889	$889	$1,389	-	14
909-011D-0006	1,873	$1,263	$1,438	$2,526	$170	20
909-011D-0007	1,580	$1,119	$1,294	$2,238	$170	18
909-011D-0013	2,001	$1,288	$1,463	$2,576	$170	19
909-011D-0229	2,904	$1,580	$1,755	$3,160	$170	100
909-011D-0280	1,868	$1,261	$1,436	$2,522	$170	75
909-011D-0311	1,988	$1,272	$1,447	$2,544	$170	40
909-011D-0342	2,368	$1,430	$1,605	$2,860	$170	64
909-011D-0347	2,910	$1,619	$1,794	$3,238	$170	13
909-011D-0606	2,301	$1,587	$1,762	$3,174	$170	94
909-011D-0637	1,744	$1,217	$1,392	$2,434	$170	96
909-011D-0640	1,834	$1,239	$1,414	$2,478	$170	46
909-011D-0649	1,605	$1,148	$1,323	$2,296	$170	80
909-011D-0655	2,707	$1,597	$1,772	$3,194	$220	97
909-011D-0660	1,704	$1,213	$1,388	$2,426	$170	55
909-011D-0662	2,460	$1,453	$1,628	$2,906	$170	34
909-011D-0664	2,576	$1,616	$1,791	$3,232	$170	74
909-013D-0134	1,496	$945	$1,045	$1,395	$195	27
909-013D-0156	1,800	$1,045	$1,145	$1,595	$195	38
909-013D-0208	953	$895	$945	$1,295	$195	10
909-013D-0217	1,500	$1,045	$1,145	$1,595	$195	31
909-013D-0226	1,800	$1,045	$1,145	$1,595	-	66
909-013D-0230	1,800	$1,045	$1,145	$1,595	$195	75
909-013D-0235	2,140	$1,195	$1,245	$1,695	$195	95
909-013D-0245	1,989	$1,045	$1,145	$1,595	$195	15
909-024D-0813	1,728	$1,728	-	$1,828	-	77
909-024D-0819	2,530	$2,530	-	$2,530	-	42
909-024D-0820	2,629	$3,180	-	$3,180	-	43
909-026D-1890	2,449	$1,025	-	$1,794	$125	60
909-026D-1939	1,635	$945	-	$1,654	$125	16
909-026D-2106	3,636	$1,230	-	$2,150	-	53
909-028D-0006	1,700	$870	$970	-	-	53
909-028D-0093	1,587	$870	$970	-	-	57
909-028D-0099	1,320	$745	$870	-	-	37
909-028D-0100	1,311	$745	$870	-	$75	78
909-028D-0103	1,520	$870	$970	-	-	39
909-028D-0109	890	$695	$770	-	-	35
909-028D-0112	1,611	$870	$970	-	-	92
909-032D-0963	1,178	$870	$830	$1,560	-	17
909-032D-1073	1,269	$950	$900	$1,630	-	99
909-032D-1135	1,788	$1,020	$970	$1,700	-	99
909-033D-0012	1,546	$1,510	$850	-	-	54
909-034D-0119	1,986	$1,510	$850	-	-	62
909-051D-0696	2,016	$1,234	$979	$1,953	-	58
909-051D-0757	1,501	$1,148	$918	$1,811	-	84
909-051D-0800	1,709	$1,148	$918	$1,811	-	74
909-051D-0960	2,784	$1,352	$1,081	$2,162	-	44
909-051D-0972	1,490	$1,107	$882	$1,744	-	21
909-051D-0974	1,736	$1,148	$918	$1,811	-	86
909-051D-0981	2,005	$1,234	$979	$1,953	-	17
909-051D-1007	4,246	$2,335	$1,783	$3,736	-	82
909-052D-0158	2,100	$989	$989	$1,589	-	11
909-055D-0748	2,525	$1,100	$1,200	$2,200	-	20
909-055D-1039	2,688	$1,550	$1,650	$3,100	-	41
909-056D-0098	3,123	$2,195	-	$3,245	-	21
909-056D-0104	1,925	$1,245	-	$2,095	-	102
909-056S-0007	3,954	$2,795	-	$3,745	-	55
909-058D-0223	1,149	$625	$560	$725	$80	103
909-076D-0280	2,585	$1,600	$995	$2,100	-	65
909-077D-0019	1,400	$1,300	$1,200	$1,725	$150	30
909-077D-0043	1,751	$1,425	$1,325	$1,850	$150	85
909-077D-0128	2,000	$1,465	$1,365	$1,990	$150	95
909-077D-0138	1,509	$1,425	$1,325	$1,850	$150	42
909-084D-0016	1,492	$950	$995	$1,850	$65	31
909-084D-0075	3,613	$1,350	$1,390	$2,300	-	81
909-084D-0081	1,631	$1,050	$1,090	$1,950	-	39
909-084D-0086	1,725	$1,050	$1,090	$1,950	-	98
909-084D-0087	3,507	$1,350	$1,390	$2,300	-	67
909-091D-0506	2,241	$2,040	$1,719	$2,723	-	47
909-091D-0507	2,486	$2,040	$1,719	$2,723	-	29
909-091D-0511	2,150	$2,040	$1,719	$2,723	-	96
909-091D-0516	2,287	$2,040	$1,719	$2,723	-	98
909-091D-0517	2,340	$2,040	$1,719	$2,723	-	14
909-091D-0523	2,514	$2,040	$1,719	$2,723	-	11
909-091D-0524	2,480	$2,040	$1,719	$2,723	-	78
909-101D-0045	1,885	$1,250	-	$2,350	-	56
909-101D-0056	2,593	$1,400	-	$2,650	-	36
909-101D-0057	2,037	$1,250	-	$2,350	-	16
909-101D-0059	2,196	$1,250	-	$2,350	-	61
909-101D-0077	2,422	$1,400	-	$2,650	-	76
909-101D-0089	2,509	$1,400	-	$2,650	-	87
909-101D-0094	2,650	$1,400	-	$2,650	-	45
909-101D-0107	2,861	$1,600	-	$2,900	-	12
909-111D-0048	1,972	$995	$1,095	$1,995	-	27
909-121D-0011	2,241	$1,089	$1,089	$1,789	$125	29
909-121D-0016	1,582	$989	$989	$1,589	$125	58
909-121D-0023	1,762	$989	$989	$1,589	$125	34
909-121D-0025	1,368	$889	$889	$1,389	$125	79
909-121D-0031	1,308	$889	$889	$1,389	-	67
909-121D-0035	1,759	$989	$989	$1,589	$125	79
909-126D-0517	1,081	$875	$716	$1,463	$105	28
909-128D-0309	1,504	$1,000	$700	-	-	80
909-130D-0394	1,581	$965	-	$1,260	-	46
909-130D-0395	1,420	$965	-	$1,260	-	63
909-141D-0038	2,700	$2,244	$2,281	$2,931	-	15
909-141D-0246	1,234	$844	$881	$1,406	-	97
909-141D-0294	2,491	$1,344	$1,381	$2,031	-	52
909-141D-0297	2,168				-	63
909-144D-0013	624	$1,040	$880	$1,440	$75	28
909-144D-0023	928	$1,040	$880	$1,440	$75	59
909-149D-0011	2,111	$1,375	$1,050	$2,350	-	19
909-152D-0084	2,806	$1,720	-	$1,720	-	81
909-155D-0047	2,500	$1,650	$1,750	$3,300	-	8
909-155D-0055	1,745	$1,100	$1,200	$2,200	-	103
909-155D-0065	1,897	$1,200	$1,300	$2,400	-	102
909-155D-0120	3,004	$1,650	$1,750	$3,300	-	93
909-155D-0170	1,897	$1,200	$1,300	$2,400	-	93
909-155D-0171	1,131	$1,000	$1,100	$2,000	-	43
909-157D-0015	2,620	$1,029	$1,134	$2,058	-	52
909-157D-0023	2,873	$1,029	$1,134	$2,058	-	26
909-159D-0007	1,850	$1,100	$1,000	$2,000	-	10
909-161D-0013	3,264	$1,995	$2,145	$2,595	-	83
909-161D-0024	3,665	$1,995	$2,195	$2,795	-	32
909-166D-0003	2,359	$1,089	$1,089	$1,789	-	92
909-167D-0001	2,017	$1,089	$1,089	$1,789	-	94
909-167D-0006	2,939	$1,189	$1,189	$1,989	-	26

<samp>104</samp>

why buy
STOCK PLANS?

Building a home yourself presents many opportunities to showcase a homeowner's creativity, individuality, and dreams turned into reality. Within these opportunities, many challenges and questions crop up. Location, size, and budget are all important to consider, as well as special features and amenities. When one really examines everything that must be determined, it can become overwhelming to search for your dream home. But, before you get too anxious, start the search process an easier way and consider choosing a home design that's a stock home plan.

Custom home plans as well as stock home plans offer positives and negatives; what is "best" can only be determined by your lifestyle, budget, and time. A customized home plan is one that a homeowner and designer or architect work together to develop from scratch, taking ideas and putting them down on paper. These plans require extra patience, as it may be months before the architect has them ready. A stock plan is a pre-developed plan that fits the needs and desires of a group of people or the general population. These are often available within days of purchasing and typically cost up to one-tenth the price of customized home plans, yet they still have all of the amenities you were looking for and usually at a much more affordable price than having custom plans drawn for you.

When compared to a customized plan, some homeowners fear that a stock home will be a carbon copy home, taking away the opportunity for individualism and creating a unique design. This is a common misconception that can waste a lot of money and time!

As you can see from the home designs throughout this book, the variety of stock plans available is truly impressive, encompassing the most up-to-date features including square footage, room dimensions, layout, and amenities. With a little patience and determination, carefully look at the numerous available stock plans throughout this book, which can be easily purchased and ready to go almost immediately.

Plus, stock plans can be customized. For example, perhaps you see a stock plan that is just about perfect, but you wish the mud room was a tad larger. Rather than go through the cost and time of having a custom home design drawn, you could have our customizing service modify the stock home plan and have your new dream plans ready to go in no time. Also, stock home plans often have a material list available, helping to eliminate unknown costs from developing during construction.

It's often a good idea to speak with someone who has recently built. Did they use stock or custom plans? What would they recommend you do, or do not undertake? Can they recommend professionals that will help you narrow down your options? As you take a look at plans throughout this publication, don't hesitate to take notes, or write down questions. Also, take advantage of our website, houseplansandmore. com. This website is very user-friendly, allowing you to search for the perfect house design by style, size, budget, and a home's features. With all of these tools readily available to you, you'll have the home design of your dreams in no time at all and with so much more ease thanks to the innovative stock plans available today that take into account your wishes in a floor plan as well as your wallet.

how can I find out if I can AFFORD to build a home?

The most important question for someone wanting to build a new home is, "How much is it going to cost?" Obviously, you must have an accurate budget set prior to ordering house plans and beginning construction, or your dream home will quickly turn into a nightmare. Our goal is to make building your dream home a much simpler reality that's within reach thanks to the estimated cost-to-build report available for all of the home plans in this book and on our website, houseplansandmore.com.

Price is always the number one factor when selecting a new home. Price dictates the size and the quality of materials you will choose. So, it comes as no surprise that having an accurate building estimate prior to making your final decision on a home plan is quite possibly the most important step in the entire process.

If you feel you've found "the" home, before taking the step of purchasing plans, order an estimated cost-to-build report for the zip code where you want to build. When you order this report created specifically for you, it will educate you on all costs associated with building your new home. Simply order the cost-to-build report on houseplansandmore.com for the home you want to build and gain knowledge of the material and labor cost associated with the home. Not only does the report allow you to choose the quality of materials, you can select options in every aspect of the project from lot condition to contractor fees. This report will allow you to successfully manage your construction budget in all areas, clearly see where the majority of the costs lie, and save you money from start to finish.

Listed to the right are the categories included in the cost-to-build report. Each category breaks down labor cost, material cost, funds needed, and the report offers the ability to manipulate over/under adjustments if necessary.

BASIC INFORMATION includes your contact information, the state and zip code where you intend to build. First, select material class. It will include details of the home such as square footage, number of windows, fireplaces, balconies, and bathrooms. Deck, basement, or bonus room square footage is included. Garage location and number of bays, and your lot size are also included.

GENERAL SOFT COSTS include cost for plans, customizing (if applicable), building permits, pre-construction services, and planning expenses.

SITE WORK & UTILITIES include water, sewer, electric, and gas. Choose the type of site work you will need prior to building and if you'll need a driveway.

FOUNDATION is selected from a menu that lists the most common types.

FRAMING ROUGH SHELL calculates your rough framing costs including framing for fireplaces, balconies, decks, porches, basements and bonus rooms.

ROOFING includes several options so you can see how it will affect your overall price.

DRY OUT SHELL allows you to select doors, windows, siding and garage doors.

ELECTRICAL includes wiring and the quality of the light fixtures.

PLUMBING includes plumbing materials, plumbing fixtures, and fire proofing materials. It includes labor costs, and the ability to change fixture quality.

HVAC includes costs for both labor and materials.

INSULATION includes costs for both labor and materials.

FINISH SHELL includes drywall, interior doors and trim, stairs, shower doors, mirrors, and bath accessories - costs for both labor and materials.

CABINETS & VANITIES select the grade of your cabinets, vanities, kitchen countertops, and bathroom vanity materials, as well as appliances.

PAINTING includes all painting materials, their quality, and labor.

FLOORING includes over a dozen flooring material options.

SPECIAL EQUIPMENT NEEDS calculate cost for unforeseen expenses.

CONTRACTOR FEE / PROJECT MANAGER includes the cost of your cost-to-build report, project manager and/or general contractor fees. If you're doing the managing yourself, your costs will be tremendously lower in this portion.

LAND PAYOFF includes the cost of your land.

RESERVES / CLOSING COSTS includes interest, contingency reserves, and closing costs.

We've taken the guesswork out of what your new home will cost. Take control of your home-building project, determine the major expenses and save money. Easily supervise all costs, from labor to materials. Manage your home building with confidence and avoid costly mistakes and unforeseen expenses. If you want to order a Cost-To-Build Report for a home plan, visit houseplansandmore.com and search for the plan. Then, look for the button that says, "Request Your Report" and get started.

what kind of **PLAN PACKAGE** do I need?

PLEASE NOTE: Not all plan packages listed below are available for every plan. Please refer to the index on page 104 in this book for a plan's options and pricing. There may be additional plan options available, please visit houseplansandmore.com, or call 1-800-373-2646 for all current plan options. The plan pricing shown in this book is subject to change without notice.

5-SET PLAN PACKAGE includes five complete sets of construction drawings. Besides one set for yourself, additional sets of blueprints will be required for your lender, your local building department, your contractor, and any other tradespeople working on your project. Please note: These 5 sets of plans are copyrighted, so they can't be altered or copied.

8-SET PLAN PACKAGE includes eight complete sets of construction drawings. Besides one set for yourself, additional sets of blueprints will be required for your lender, your local building department, your contractor, and any other tradespeople working on your project. Please note: These 8 sets of plans are copyrighted, so they can't be altered or copied.

REPRODUCIBLE MASTER is one complete paper set of construction drawings that can be modified. They include a one-time build copyright release that allows you to draw changes on the plans. This allows you, your builder, or local design professional to make the necessary drawing changes without the major expense of entirely redrawing the plans. Easily make minor drawing changes by using correction fluid to cover up small areas of the existing drawing, then draw in your modifications. Once the plan has been altered to fit your needs, you have the right to copy, or reproduce the modified plans as needed for building your home. Please note: The right of building only one home from these plans is licensed exclusively to the buyer. You may not use this design to build a second or multiple dwelling(s) without purchasing a multi-build license.

PDF FILE FORMAT is our most popular plan option because of how fast you can receive them (usually within 24 to 48 hours Monday through Friday), and their ability to be easily shared via email with your contractor, subcontractors, and local building officials. The PDF file format is a complete set of construction drawings in an electronic file format. It includes a one-time build copyright release that allows you to make changes and copies of the plans. Typically you will receive a PDF file via email within 24-48 hours (Mon-Fri, 7:30am-4:30pm CST) allowing you to save money on shipping. Upon receiving, visit a local copy or print shop and print the number of plans you need to build your home, or print one and alter the plan by using correction fluid and drawing in your modifications. Please note: These are flat image files and cannot be altered electronically. PDF files are non-refundable and not returnable.

CAD FILE FORMAT is the actual computer files for a plan directly from AutoCAD, or another computer aided design program. CAD files are the best option if you have a significant amount of changes to make to the plan, or if you need to make the plan fit your local codes. If you purchase a CAD File, it allows you, or a local design professional the ability to modify the plans electronically in a CAD program, so making changes to the plan is easier and less expensive than using a paper set of plans when modifying. A CAD package also includes a one-time build copyright release that allows you to legally make your changes, and print multiple copies of the plan. See the specific plan page for availability and pricing. Please note: CAD files are non-refundable and not returnable.

MIRROR REVERSE SETS Sometimes a home fits a site better if it is flipped left to right. A mirror reverse set of plans is simply a mirror image of the original drawings causing the lettering and dimensions to read backwards. Therefore, when ordering a mirror reverse set of plans, you must purchase at least one set of the original plans to read from, and use the mirror reverse set for construction. Some plans offer right reading reverse for an additional fee. This means the plan has been redrawn by the designer as the mirrored version and can easily be read.

ADDITIONAL SETS You can order additional sets of a plan for an additional fee. A 5-set, 8-set, or reproducible master must have been previously purchased. Please note: Only available within 90 days after purchase of a plan package.

2" X 6" EXTERIOR WALLS 2" x 6" exterior walls can be purchased for some plans for an additional fee (see houseplansandmore.com for availability and pricing).

our PLAN PACKAGES include...

Quality plans for building your future, with extras that provide unsurpassed value, ensure good construction and long-term enjoyment. A quality home - one that looks good, functions well, and provides years of enjoyment - is a product of many things - design, materials, and craftsmanship. But it's also the result of outstanding blueprints - the actual plans and specifications that tell the builder exactly how to build your home.

And with our BLUEPRINT PACKAGES you get the absolute best. A complete set of blueprints is available for every design in this book. These "working drawings" are highly detailed, resulting in two key benefits:

- **BETTER UNDERSTANDING BY THE CONTRACTOR OF HOW TO BUILD YOUR HOME AND...**

- **MORE ACCURATE CONSTRUCTION ESTIMATES THAT WILL SAVE YOU TIME AND MONEY.**

Below is a sample of the plan information included for most of the designs in this book. Specific details may vary with each designer's plan. While this information is typical of most plans, we cannot assure the inclusion of all the following referenced items. Please contact us at 1-800-373-2646 for a plan's specific information, including which of the following items are included.

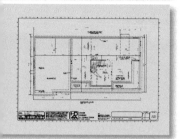

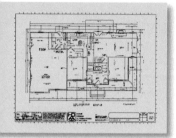

1 cover sheet is included with many of the plans, the cover sheet is the artist's rendering of the exterior of the home. It will give you an idea of how your home will look when completed and landscaped.

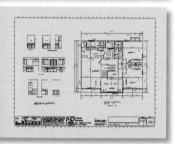

2 foundation plan shows the layout of the basement, walk-out basement, crawl space, slab or pier foundation. All necessary notations and dimensions are included. See plan page for the foundation types included. If the home plan you choose does not have your desired foundation type, our Customer Service Representatives can advise you on how to customize your foundation to suit your specific needs or site conditions.

3 floor plans show the placement of walls, doors, closets, plumbing fixtures, electrical outlets, columns, and beams for each level of the home.

4 interior elevations provide views of special interior elements such as fireplaces, kitchen cabinets, built-in units and other features of the home.

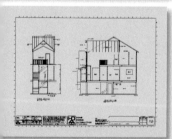

5 exterior elevations illustrate the front, rear and both sides of the house, with all details of exterior materials and the required dimensions.

6 sections show detail views of the home or portions of the home as if it were sliced from the roof to the foundation. This sheet shows important areas such as load-bearing walls, stairs, joists, trusses and other structural elements, which are critical for proper construction.

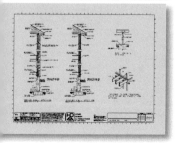

7 details show how to construct certain components of your home, such as the roof system, stairs, deck, etc.

do you want to make CHANGES to your plan?

We understand that sometimes it is difficult to find blueprints that meet all of your specific needs.
That is why we offer home plan modification services so you can build a home exactly the way you want it!

ARE YOU THINKING ABOUT CUSTOMIZING A PLAN?

If you're like many customers, you may want to make changes to your home plan to make it the dream home you've always wanted. That's where our expert design and modification partners come in. You won't find a more efficient and economic way to get your changes done than by using our home plan customizing services.

Whether it's enlarging a kitchen, adding a porch, or converting a crawl space to a basement, we can customize any plan and make it perfect for your needs. Simply create your wish list and let us go to work. Soon you'll have the blueprints for your new home and at a fraction of the cost of hiring a local architect!

IT'S EASY!

- We can customize any of plans in this book.
- We provide a FREE cost estimate for your home plan modifications within 24-48 hours (Monday through Friday).
- Average turn-around time to complete the modifications is typically 2-3 weeks.
- You will receive one-on-one design consultations.

CUSTOMIZING FACTS

- The average cost to have a house plan customized is typically less than 1 percent of the building costs — compare that to the national average of 7 percent of building costs.
- The average modification cost for a home is typically $800 to $1,500. This does not include the cost of purchasing the PDF file format of the blueprints, which is required to legally make plan changes.

OTHER HELPFUL INFORMATION

- Sketch, or make a specific list of changes you'd like to make on the Home Plan Modification Request Form.
- One of our home plan modification specialists will contact you within 24-48 hours with your free estimate.
- Upon accepting the estimate, you will need to purchase the PDF or CAD file format.
- A contract, which includes a specific list of changes and fees will be sent to you prior for your approval.
- Upon approving the contract, our design partners will keep you up to date by emailing sketches throughout the project.
- Plans can be converted to metric, or to a Barrier-free layout (also referred to as a universal home design, which allows easy mobility for an individual with limitations of any kind).

2 EASY STEPS

1 visit houseplansandmore.com or scan the QR code here to download the Home Plan Modification Request Form.

2 email your completed form to: customizehpm@designamerica.com, or fax it to: 651-602-5050. If you are not able to access the Internet, please call 1-800-373-2646 (Monday through Friday).

helpful **BUILDING AIDS**

Your Blueprint Package will contain all of the necessary construction information you need to build your home. But, we also offer the following products and services to save you time and money in the building process.

MATERIAL LIST Many of the home plans in this book have a material list available for purchase that gives you the quantity, dimensions, and description of the building materials needed to construct the home (see the specific plan page for availability and pricing). Keep in mind, due to variations in local building code requirements, exact material quantities cannot be guaranteed. Note: Material lists are created with the standard foundation type only. Please review the material list and the construction drawings with your material supplier to verify measurements and quantities of the materials listed before ordering supplies.

THE LEGAL KIT Avoid many legal pitfalls and build your home with confidence using the forms and contracts featured in this kit. Included are request for proposal documents, various fixed price and cost plus contracts, instructions on how and when to use each form, warranty statements and more. Save time and money before you break ground on your new home or start a remodeling project. All forms are reproducible. This kit is ideal for homebuilders and contractors. Cost: $35.00

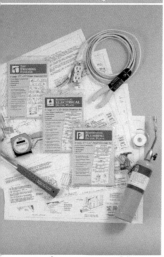

DETAIL PLAN PACKAGES - FRAMING, ELECTRICAL & PLUMBING Three separate packages offer homebuilders details for constructing various foundations; numerous floor, wall and roof framing techniques; simple to complex residential wiring; sump and water softener hookups; plumbing connection methods; installation of septic systems, and more. Each package includes three dimensional illustrations and a glossary of terms. Purchase one or all three. Cost: $20.00 each or all three for $40.00 Please note: These drawings do not pertain to a specific home plan, but they include general guidelines and tips for construction in all 3 of these trades.

EXPRESS DELIVERY Most orders are processed within 24 hours of receipt. Please allow 7-10 business days for standard delivery. If you need to place a rush order, please call us by 11:00 am Monday through Friday CST and ask for express service (allow 1-2 business days). Please see page 111 for specific pricing information for shipping and handling.

TECHNICAL ASSISTANCE If you have questions about your blueprints, we offer technical assistance by calling 1-314-770-2228 (Monday through Friday). Whether it involves design modifications or field assistance, our home plans team is extremely familiar with all of our designs and will be happy to help you. We want your home to be everything you expect it to be.

before you ORDER

PLEASE NOTE: Plan pricing is subject to change without notice. For current pricing, visit houseplansandmore.com, or call us at 1-800-373-2646.

BUILDING CODE REQUIREMENTS At the time the construction drawings were prepared, every effort was made to ensure that these plans and specifications met nationally recognized codes. These plans conform to most national building codes. Because building codes vary from area to area, some drawing modifications and/or the assistance of a professional designer or architect may be necessary to comply with your local codes, or to accommodate your specific building site conditions. We advise you to consult with your local building official, or a local builder for information regarding codes governing your area prior to ordering blueprints.

COPYRIGHT Plans are protected under Copyright Law. Reproduction by any means is strictly prohibited. The right of building only one structure from all plan packages is licensed exclusively to the buyer and the plans may not be resold unless by express written authorization from the home designer, or architect. You may not use this design to build a second or multiple structure(s) without purchasing a multi-build license. Each violation of the Copyright Law is punishable in a fine.

LICENSE TO BUILD When you purchase a "full set of construction drawings" from Design America, Inc., you are purchasing an exclusive one-time "License to Build," not the rights to the design. Design America, Inc. is granting you permission on behalf of the plan's designer or architect to use the construction drawings one-time for the building of the home. The construction drawings (also referred to as blueprints/plans and any derivative of that plan whether extensive or minor) are still owned and protected under copyright laws by the original designer. The blueprints/plans cannot be resold, transferred, rented, loaned or used by anyone other than the original purchaser of the "License to Build" without written consent from Design America, Inc. or the plan designer. If you are interested in building the plan more than once, please call 1-800-373-2646 and inquire about purchasing a Multi-Build License that will allow you to build a home design more than one time. Please note: A "full set of construction drawings" consists of either CAD files or PDF files.

shipping & handling charges

U.S. SHIPPING

(AK and HI express only)

Regular (allow 7-10 business days)	$30.00
Priority (allow 3-5 business days)	$50.00
Express* (allow 1-2 business days)	$70.00

CANADA SHIPPING**

Regular (allow 8-12 business days)	$50.00
Express* (allow 3-5 business days)	$100.00

OVERSEAS SHIPPING / INTERNATIONAL

Call, fax, or e-mail (customerservice@designamerica.com) for shipping costs.

* For express delivery please call us by 11:00 am Monday-Friday CST

** Orders may be subject to custom's fees and or duties/taxes.

Note: Shipping and handling charges do not apply on PDF Files and CAD File orders. PDF and CAD orders will be emailed within 24-48 hours (Monday - Friday, 7:30 am - 4:30 pm CST) of purchase.

EXCHANGE POLICY Since blueprints are printed in response to your order, we cannot honor requests for refunds or returns.

ORDER FORM

Please send me the following:

Plan Number: 909-_____

Select Foundation Type:

(Select ONE- see plan page for available options).

☐ Slab   ☐ Crawl space   ☐ Basement

☐ Walk-out basement   ☐ Pier

☐ Optional Foundation for an additional fee

   Enter foundation cost here $ _____

COST

PLAN PACKAGE

☐ CAD File $ _____

☐ PDF File Format (recommended) $ _____

☐ Reproducible Masters $ _____

☐ 8-Set Plan Package $ _____

☐ 5-Set Plan Package $ _____

See the index on page 104 for the most commonly ordered plan packages, or visit houseplansandmore.com to see current pricing and all plan package options available.

IMPORTANT EXTRAS

For pricing and availability of Material Lists, see the plan page. For the other plan options listed below, visit houseplansandmore.com, or call 1-800-373-2646.

☐ Additional plan sets*:

   _____ set(s) at $_____ per set $ _____

☐ Print in right-reading reverse:

   one-time additional fee of $_____ $ _____

☐ Print in mirror reverse:

   _____ set(s) at $_____ per set $ _____

   (where right reading reverse is not available)

☐ Material list (see the index on page 104) $ _____

☐ Legal Kit (001D-9991, see page 110) $ _____

Detail Plan Packages: (see page 110)

   ☐ Framing   ☐ Electrical   ☐ Plumbing $ _____

   (001D-9992)   (001D-9993)   (001D-9994)

SUBTOTAL $ _____

Sales Tax (MO residents only, add 8.113%) $ _____

☐ Shipping (see page 111) $ _____

TOTAL $ _____

*Available only within 90 days after purchase of plan.

HELPFUL TIPS

- You can upgrade to a different plan package within 90 days of your original plan purchase.
- Additional sets cannot be ordered without the purchase of a 5-Set, 8-Set, or Reproducible Masters

Name _____

                (Please print or type)

Street _____

            (Please do not use a P.O. Box)

City _____ State _____

Country _____ Zip _____

Daytime telephone   (_____) _____

E-Mail _____

      (For invoice and tracking information)

PAYMENT ☐ Bank check/money order. No personal checks.

Make checks payable to Design America, Inc.

☐ MasterCard   ☐ VISA   ☐ DISCOVER   ☐ American Express Cards

Credit card number_____

Expiration date (mm/yy)_____CID _____

Signature _____

☐ I hereby authorize Design America, Inc. to charge this purchase to my credit card.

Please check the appropriate box:

☐ Building home for myself

☐ Building home for someone else

ORDER ONLINE

houseplansandmore.com

ORDER TOLL-FREE BY PHONE

1-800-373-2646

Fax: 314-770-2226

EXPRESS DELIVERY

Most orders are processed within 24 hours of receipt. If you need to place a rush order, please call us by 11:00 am CST and ask for express service. Business Hours: Monday - Friday 7:30 am-4:30 pm.

MAIL YOUR ORDER

Design America, Inc.

734 West Port Plaza, Suite #208

St. Louis, MO 63146

One-Story Home Plans **SOURCE CODE** 909

Made in the USA
Columbia, SC
21 March 2022

57947349R00064